ISO 9000:2000
Auditor Questions

David Hoyle
John Thompson

Transition Support
A flexible approach to business improvement

Published by:
Transition Support Ltd
Royal Monnow
Redbrook Road
Monmouth
Monmouthshire
NP25 3LY
Tel/Fax: 00 44 01600 716509
E-mail mail@transition-support.com
Web site http://www.transition-support.com

First published January 2001

Reprinted May 2001

Reprinted April 2002

ISBN 1-903417-04-X

Printed and bound Great Britain by Biddles Ltd *www.biddles.co.uk*

Contents

The past has only got us to where we are today ....*it may not necessarily get us to where we want to be!*

Foreword

The issue of ISO 9000:2000 brought a fundamental change in how the application of the requirements of the Standard related to an organization's approach to Quality Management. The focus on how the organization achieves its objectives through a set of interconnected processes also brought a fundamental change in the approach to auditing. Auditing to the new Standard needs be radically different to that used to audit against previous versions where the approach concentrated on compliance to specific and individual requirements, independently of how the system really contributed to achieving the organization's objectives - a radical change indeed.

Organizations and the writers of Standards alike recognised that change was needed and in September 1999 a joint communiqué from the IAF, ISO/TC176 and ISO/CASCO laid down some new and potentially far-reaching requirements addressing Certification Body auditors. This required auditors to demonstrate their knowledge and understanding of the 8 Quality management principles. Auditors are now required to establish that the systems they are auditing have been based on these principles one of which is the *process approach*.

The purpose of this book is to provide an effective questioning technique that will enable auditors to establish that an organization is managing its processes effectively. This radical new approach to auditing focuses on performance relative to objectives - not simply on compliance. Auditing will produce results that will now attract the attention of Management simply because audits are aligned with the *real purpose* of management – to improve the organization's capability to satisfy its customers and other interested parties.

This book provides auditors with a new approach that will enable them to keep the focus on the real purpose. At the core of this new approach are five fundamental questions upon which the process approach is based. From these a series of questions are derived for several business processes that will reveal the evidence needed to demonstrate compliance with ISO 9001:2000. At the same time the robustness of the organization's processes to achieve their objectives is tested. The Quality management principles are explained to show how they can be used to establish that the organization's management system is soundly based. The current auditing approaches are evaluated to show the fundamental weaknesses relative to how audits are planned, conducted and reported. This book contains lots of questions for auditors, structured around key business processes and linked to the requirements of the Standard.

Where the 1994 version of a standard in the ISO 9000 family is referred to, the date is mentioned but for all other references to the ISO 9000:2000 family of standards the year 2000 has been dropped.

Auditing is a skill that can only be learnt through practice. The proficiency of the auditor is determined not by an ability to rattle off a set of questions and record the results, but firstly by having a clear idea of what is to be accomplished and secondly by asking questions that will reveal information of use to management. It is hoped that the reader will develop a clear idea and make the transition to a more effective method of auditing. We do not expect auditors to change tactics overnight but if a few learn this new technique and organizations benefit from their audits we will have achieved our goal.

Chapter 1

Introduction

In 1983 the thrust of the message in the UK Government's White Paper on Standards, Quality and International Competitiveness was that British Industry should utilize national standards and quality assurance as a means to improve its competitiveness. The quality system standards used to spearhead this campaign were born out of the defence industry where there was a long tradition of command and control. As a consequence, ISO 9000 followed the same pattern of imposing requirements to prevent failures that experience had shown led to poor product quality. This approach adopted in the early 1980s by a few thousand organizations, mainly in the UK has grown to a few hundred thousand organizations worldwide.

During this time there has been a growing recognition that quality does not result from simply imposing rules, but from the need for organizations to create and maintain an environment in which people are motivated to do the right things right without having to be told. ISO 9000 now reflects that recognition. The bureaucracy has been replaced by 8 Quality management principles that (in the words of ISO 9000) *aim to help organizations to achieve sustained success.*

For the designers and managers of the organization's quality management system these principles are the key to a successful implementation of ISO 9000.

For the auditors they are the key to transforming the way quality system audits are conducted, as recognised by the International Accreditation Forum (IAF).

In response to ISO 9000:1994 most organizations created documentation that focused only on those requirements which were addressed by the Standard. The belief was that by documenting what you do and doing what you document against each specific requirement in the Standard, product quality would improve. As some of the principal factors affecting the quality of output were missing, conformity with ISO 9001:1994 did not stop organizations avoiding quality problems.

This narrow view of quality management has now been swept aside by ISO 9000:2000 and in its place it encourages (in the words of ISO 9000) *organizations to:*

a)   *determine the needs and expectations of customers and other interested parties;*

b)   *establish the quality policy and quality objectives of the organization;*

c)   *determine the processes and responsibilities necessary to attain the quality objectives;*

d)   *determine and provide the resources necessary to attain the quality objectives;*

e)   *establish methods to measure the effectiveness and efficiency of each process;*

f)   *apply these measures to determine the effectiveness and efficiency of each process;*

g)   *determine means of preventing nonconformities and eliminating their causes;*

h)   *establish and apply a process for continual improvement of the quality management system.*

This simple, yet powerful message is there for all to see and understand. However, one might be forgiven (but only momentarily) for missing it if on reading the Standard one only looks for and sees many of the old familiar phrases. We are creatures of habit and tend to resist change.

It does appear that the committees involved in drafting the Standard tried to put as many of the old requirements as they could into the new version. It is clear that an opportunity was missed to create a far simpler, shorter Standard, even reducing it to a page or two, which would have enabled everyone to see a clear line of sight from the Standard to customer satisfaction. It would have been a far more effective design tool and auditing tool for it is the detail requirements that cause auditors to loose sight of the objectives.

Over the previous 17 years the certification bodies have pursued an approach of raising nonconformities because either the words in the Standard have not been met or the organization has not done what it said it would do. There has been no examination of output results, but it is the improvement of these results that will improve the competitiveness of industry not conformity with procedures. Organizations continue with the conformity approach to auditing because Certification Bodies do the same. Now organizations must change the focus of their quality management system and auditors must change their approach.

The IAF now requires external auditors to demonstrate knowledge of the Quality management principles and the concepts and terminology of the Standards. This will require a change in questioning technique.

No longer will auditors open their questioning with:

*"Have you got a procedure for *******? – Show me"*

It is more likely to be:

*"What improvement in results was obtained from your last review of the ******** process? – Show me"*

We call this new technique the *process approach to auditing.*

It is simple but powerful!

Chapter 2

Audit methodologies

Although the audits conducted under the umbrella of ISO 9000 or quality management are intended to be quality audits rather than financial audits the trend has been that quality audits focus on procedures and not on quality. Quality, cost and delivery are inextricably linked and yet auditors in general do not examine costs or the extent to which products and services are delivered on time. Quality is a result. It is determined by the extent to which an outcome meets the needs of those for whom it is provided. If the outcome fails to satisfy these needs, the outcome is of poor quality. If the outcome meets the needs it is of good quality. However, since the launch of ISO 9000, quality auditing within certification bodies and most certificated organizations has ignored the outcomes and whether those for whom they are provided are satisfied. The quest in most cases has been to place a 'tick in a box' leaving the question of performance unexplored and hence unchallenged. As a result, auditors fill the boxes with ticks and the organization gets the badge regardless of its actual performance. Hence the retort, "You can produce rubbish and still obtain ISO 9000 certification provided the rubbish is consistent rubbish."

The approach taken by many auditors, both internal and external has been conditioned by training and observation. Most auditors have been exposed to conformity auditing where the sole objective is to establish if a specific requirement has been met. However, the requirement has often not been focused on a performance result or output but has been focused on a task. To illustrate this point ISO 9001:1994 clause 4.5.3 required changes to documents and data to be reviewed and approved. The auditor generally looked to establish that a procedure existed that required such action and proceeded to examine changes for evidence that these had been reviewed and approved. Having found the evidence, it was assumed that the requirement had been met. One swallow does not make a summer, therefore the auditor may have looked for other document changes to check that they too had been reviewed and approved. After gathering the evidence, the auditor made a conformity judgement - not a performance judgement - that documents were reviewed and approved for adequacy prior to issue. The auditor probably did not search for the approval criteria or for evidence that the people concerned were competent to approve the change or for evidence that the change was indeed necessary - that it would improve performance! So how could a decision be made that the documents are in fact adequate - i.e. fit for their intended purpose? The decision is usually made from the evidence that those who approved the documents were authorized to do so. The audit revolves around documents and whether or not they are approved - not whether the information needed to perform the job is available and its integrity is assured.

It has been this pre-occupation with approval of documents and tasks that has contributed to the statement that ISO 9000 and Quality Management systems are bureaucratic nightmares that add no real value to the organization and generate 'nit-picking' auditors.

In general, the questions any auditors ask are conditioned by the plan they have developed and the strategy taken to discover the answers. There are a number of approaches generally used in conducting internal and external quality system audits and each can be characterised by:

- ♦ the way the audit is planned (this affects what the auditor looks at and the order in which the audit is performed)
- ♦ the way check lists are produced (this affects what the auditor looks for and the questions the auditor will ask)
- ♦ the way the auditor conducts the audit (this affects the speed at which evidence is collected and its significance determined)
- ♦ the way the auditor reaches conclusions (this affects the validity of the results).

As each organization conducting audits will have evolved its own techniques there are no definitive methods but what follows illustrates the distinguishing features of three generic approaches. Only those aspects of the audit that relate to the auditor's questions are addressed. The preparation, analysis and reporting activities are omitted.

The element approach

With the element approach the auditor uses the elements of the governing Standard, eg ISO 9001:1994, as the basis for planning and conducting the audit. An element in this context is a subsection of the Standard of which there are 20 in section 4 of ISO 9001:1994.

Approach to planning the audit

The audit plan follows the elements of the Standard such that it commences with an examination of element 4.1 on Management Responsibility and ends with an examination of element 4.20 on Statistical Techniques. The audit schedule may not follow the elements in a numerical order as this will depend upon location and timing, but in principle, each element is matched with a person or department within the organization. When the auditor arrives in the selected department, the audit scope is limited to establishing conformity only with those requirements that are addressed by the corresponding element of the standard.. Although many elements apply to each department the auditor primarily focuses on the most appropriate element for that department. The only departments in the plan are those that are perceived to be within the scope of the registration. An example is shown in Table 2.1.

Table 2.1 Element-based audit plan

Element	Title	Department	Auditor	Time
4.1	Management responsibility	General manager		
4.2	Quality system	Quality		
4.3	Contract review	Sales		
4.4	Design control	Design		
4.5	Document and data control	Quality		
4.6	Purchasing	Purchasing		
4.7	Customer supplied product	Production		
4.8	Product identification & traceability	Production		
4.9	Process control	Production		
4.10	Inspection and test	Inspection		
4.11	Inspection, measuring and test equipment	Calibration		
4.12	Inspection and test status	Inspection		
4.13	Nonconforming material	Inspection		
4.14	Corrective and preventive action	Quality		
4.15	Handling, storage, packaging, preservation and delivery	Shipping		
4.16	Control of quality records	Quality		
4.17	Internal quality audit	Quality		
4.18	Training	Personnel		
4.19	Servicing	Servicing		
4.20	Statistical techniques	Production		

Approach to check lists

The check lists tend to be complied by taking each 'shall' statement and rewriting the requirement of the Standard in the form of a question. This approach is applied in external audits (second and third party) and internal system audits.

Approach to audit conduct

The auditor commences the audit by asking the first question off the check list. Hence if the requirement is for the quality policy to be defined, the auditor would ask "What is your quality policy?" followed by "Where is the policy defined?" and possibly "Who defined this policy?" If a document is produced this might be followed by "Who approved this and how do you know it is up to date?", illustrating that Document Control (Element 4.5) is not far away.

The auditors tend to look for specific evidence in the belief that if they find it, the organization is compliant. For example when seeking compliance with element 4.3 on contract review, the auditor would ask "Have you got a procedure for contract review?" When shown the procedure the auditor would examine to see if it covered the other requirements in element 4.3 of the Standard and then ask to see some records of contract review. When satisfied the records provided evidence that the requirements had been addressed the auditor would move on to the next element. If a record could not be found or a signature was missing or a record was not in the format the organization specified in its procedure, a nonconformity report would be issued.

Approach to conclusions

The auditor seeks nonconformity and reaches a conclusion on the number of nonconformities found in the samples taken. The auditor often seeks one example to test compliance in one area and bases decisions on whether conformity was found. Sometimes an auditor will examine several pieces of evidence seeking nonconformity and when one is found, go no further. Often the search stops at the department boundary. Nonconformities are classified on the basis that if a requirement of the Standard has not been met, no matter how insignificant, a major nonconformity is issued. If a procedure has not been followed and the requirement in the procedure is not one addressed by the Standard then a minor nonconformity is issued.

Advantages of the element approach

The element approach:

- ♦ is simple to use
- ♦ it can be learnt by almost anyone
- ♦ requires little understanding of the organization
- ♦ is favoured by accreditation bodies
- ♦ is easily verified by examination of audit reports
- ♦ creates a high degree of consistency
- ♦ lends itself to scoring using a numerical scale
- ♦ it puts the badge on the wall.

Disadvantages of the element approach

The approach is not effective because:

- ♦ the effectiveness of the system is not determined
- ♦ there is no assessment of the results which the system delivers
- ♦ conformity with requirements that apply to more than one department is not tested apart from Document Control
- ♦ linkages between departments are not tested
- ♦ linkages between processes are not tested
- ♦ the questions in the check list are theoretical and will not be the actual questions asked
- ♦ the checks will not follow the flow of work through the organization
- ♦ if used rigidly, it will confuse the auditee as to what the auditor is trying to establish
- ♦ if the checks are not tailored to the specific organization, the auditee will get the impression that the auditor is not interested in understanding how the organization functions
- ♦ the quest is for documentation and not effectiveness
- ♦ the focus is on conformity with the written procedures
- ♦ it is assumed that conformity with requirements is indicative that the operations are under control
- ♦ the auditor overlooks the factors that will determine that the operations are under control and that the controls are effective
- ♦ there is little examination of product or process
- ♦ no judgement is made on the significance of the findings
- ♦ there is no test for frequency of occurrence
- ♦ there is no examination in other areas to see if problems identified are deep rooted

- ◆ there is no search for the root cause
- ◆ there is an assumption that correcting any nonconformity will improve organizational effectiveness
- ◆ auditors need to be familiar with the industry to know what to look for.

As a result there is little added value. The auditor rarely finds problems of which the organization is not already aware. It results in a paper chase and time spent correcting minor problems that have little impact on organizational effectiveness.

The departmental approach

With the departmental approach, the auditor starts with the organization's departments and seeks conformity with those requirements of the Standard that apply to each department. Internal and external auditors use this approach.

Approach to planning the audit

The audit plan is based on the organization chart, with those departments that come within the scope of registration being allotted timeslots in the audit schedule. As with the element approach, Management Responsibility still features in departmental audits and is allotted to General Management. However, requirements within element 4.1 are tested in each department. A typical departmental audit plan is illustrated in Table 2.2.

In practice the auditor may not check conformity with all requirement that apply to a particular department but the chances are that evidence of conformity will be gathered from more than one department.

Table 2.2 Department-based audit plan

Date	Management	Quality	Sales	Design	Purchasing	Production	Inspection	Shipping	Calibration	Personnel	Servicing
4.20						●	●				
4.19											●
4.18		●	●	●	●	●	●	●	●	●	●
4.17		●									
4.16	●	●	●	●	●	●	●	●	●	●	●
4.15						●	●	●			
4.14		●	●	●	●	●	●	●	●	●	●
4.13						●	●				
4.12						●	●				
4.11						●	●		●		
4.10							●				
4.9						●	●				
4.8						●					
4.7						●					
4.6		●			●						
4.5	●	●	●	●	●	●	●	●	●	●	●
4.4				●							
4.3			●								
4.2		●		●		●					
4.1	●	●	●	●	●	●	●	●	●	●	●

Auditor

Department

Approach to check lists

The checklists tend to be compiled by collecting the relevant element check lists together and putting them in some sort of order that will allow the auditor to follow a trail through the department. With internal audits, the focus is on checking conformity with procedures and therefore the check list will identify the general company procedures and relevant departmental procedures that apply.

Checklists often cite questions taken from the requirements of the Standard but will pick up additional questions from the departmental procedures.

Approach to audit conduct

The auditor seeks out the department manager and asks questions from the checklist related to the procedures issued for that department. As many more elements of the Standard are addressed in each department the auditor will jump from requirement to requirement and may follow trails through the department but will stop at the department boundary. The objective is to establish whether the department's staff follow the documented procedures and so the trails will be dictated by linkages between procedures signalled by cross references within each procedure. For example when examining a procedure or an instruction the auditor may look for evidence that the document is under control, has a signature, has a revision status etc. Questions also tend to contain the expected result such as "Where do you get your instructions from?" implying that they should come from somewhere, "Where are the results of those checks recorded?" - implying that results should be recorded and "What is the quality policy?" - implying that the person should know the quality policy.

Approach to conclusions

The auditor using the departmental approach may seek conformity and in doing so stumble across a nonconformity. As with the element approach the auditor may only take one sample in testing conformity. If the evidence presented in response to the questions conforms to the procedure, the procedure is assumed to be implemented and effective.

Advantages of the departmental approach

The departmental approach:

- ◆ checks compliance with the requirements in the areas to which they apply
- ◆ follows work flow through a department
- ◆ focuses on departmental issues and hence will cause less confusion
- ◆ focuses on departmental processes and products
- ◆ puts the badge on the wall.

The weakness of departmental approach

The approach is not effective because:

- ◆ the effectiveness of the system is not determined
- ◆ there is no assessment of the results which the system delivers
- ◆ linkages between departments are not tested
- ◆ linkages between processes are not tested
- ◆ the questions in the check list are theoretical and will not be the actual questions asked
- ◆ the checks are focused on conformity not effectiveness
- ◆ the quest is for documentation and not effectiveness
- ◆ the focus is on conformity with the written procedures
- ◆ it is assumed that conformity with procedures is indicative that the operations are under control
- ◆ no judgement is made on the significance of the findings
- ◆ there is no test for frequency of occurrence
- ◆ there is no examination in other departments to see if problems identified are deep rooted
- ◆ there is no search for the root cause
- ◆ there is an assumption that correcting any nonconformity will improve organizational effectiveness
- ◆ auditors need some knowledge of the industry to know how to generate questions from procedures and what to look for.

Task based approach

The task-based approach is not dissimilar to the departmental approach and may well be used on a departmental basis. With this approach the auditor identifies the work areas to visit and on arrival seeks to establish what tasks are performed there. The auditor then proceeds to gather facts about the task in terms of the person performing or supervising the task, items being worked on, equipment used to perform the task and information used or generated by the task. The auditor will tend to make notes of items to be checked elsewhere, eg a person's name (so that a training record might be checked), an equipment number (so that its calibration status might be checked). The primary difference is that the task approach uses a task element framework as the basis for revealing evidence rather than a set of requirements such as ISO 9000.

Approach to planning the audit

The task-based approach would be planned in the same way as departmental audits but could be based on a series of work areas regardless of which department they were located. The plan starts with the customer requirements proceeds through all the work areas that lead to completed output.

Approach to check lists

Check lists would focus on a particular task and identify the questions relative to the four tasks elements (person, item, equipment, information). Often a flow chart is used in planning the check list, either taken from the organization's procedures or drawn by the auditor.

Approach to audit conduct

The auditor interviews an individual to establish that the tasks being performed are compliant with the requirements for the task. The audit may commence at the starting point for a contract, product or project and proceed forwards to completion, or may start with the end result and trace backwards through all relevant work areas to the starting point.

Approach to conclusions

The auditor using the task-based approach would seek out sufficient examples to prove conformity with the requirements but the focus remains on whether the tasks have been performed in accordance with the requirements. The approach reveals not only whether procedures have been followed but whether the procedures adequately address the requirements of the governing standards. As the requirements may tend to be very prescriptive, evidence will be gathered relative to each instruction resulting in the nonconformities addressing trivia as well as major loop holes in the system.

Advantages of the task based approach

The task approach:

- ♦ checks compliance with the requirements along a trail from start to finish
- ♦ follows work flow through a department
- ♦ tests linkages between departments
- ♦ uses check lists which seek to establish adequate control over operations
- ♦ focuses on departmental processes and products
- ♦ reveals problems with people, items, information and equipment
- ♦ attempts to determine the effectiveness of the system in terms of conformity.

The weakness of task based approach

The approach is not effective because:

- ♦ there is no assessment of the results which the system delivers
- ♦ it does not examine the performance of processes
- ♦ the checks are focused on conformity not effectiveness
- ♦ the focus is on conformity with requirements
- ♦ no judgement is made on the significance of the findings
- ♦ there is no search for the root cause
- ♦ there is an assumption that correcting any nonconformity will improve organizational effectiveness
- ♦ auditors need to be familiar with the industry to know what to look for.

Process approach is fundamentally different

With the process approach the auditor believes that the purpose of carrying out work is to produce a desired outcome and uses an audit to determine whether that work is effectively managed to achieve that outcome. The auditor seeks to establish the results the organization desires to achieve, determines that these results take into account the needs of the interested parties and then examines the way that processes are managed to achieve these results and improve performance.

Approach to planning the audit

The audit plan is based on the processes that achieve the organization's objectives and requires the auditor to know what these processes are prior to conducting the audit. There are some processes that are common to all organizations such as business management, marketing, sales, and resource management but the product/service generation processes differ relative to the type of products and services the organization provides. Although the plan is based on processes and not based on elements or departments, the organization structure is useful only in identifying who to interview. The plan would therefore show a path through business processes that cut across departmental boundaries.

Approach to check lists

The process approach does not require a detailed checklist, as the framework used can be adapted to any process. The auditor does not undertake the role of a technical expert therefore checks for specific technical issues are unnecessary. However the lack of robustness in addressing technical issues can be exposed through systematically following the approach.

Approach to audit conduct

The audit commences with top management and examines the business management process. The information acquired is then used as the basis for establishing whether the organization's processes are being managed effectively. The auditor proceeds through the resource management processes first, gathering information and making linkages. If the Human Resource Management process is found effective it will feed competent people to other processes, thus removing the specific need to check training eg when checking the Sales process. If the physical resource management process is found effective it too will feed capable equipment, components etc to other processes removing the need to check in each process. Once the resource management processes are found to be effective the auditor proceeds through the chain of processes from marketing to delivery. The questions are simple and in a very short period the auditor can determine whether the organization is managing its processes effectively.

Approach to conclusions

The auditor is looking for conformity but the requirements are treated as a means to an end not the end in themselves. The auditor is looking for evidence that the organization's processes are being managed effectively and in doing so will touch almost every requirement in ISO 9001. If evidence is revealed that the organization is satisfying its customers and other interested parties and is applying the 8 principles of quality management in the way it runs the business there will be no sound basis for reporting nonconformities. If the organization had not defined objectives for its processes, was not measuring process performance and was not improving output quality and process effectiveness, there would be grounds for raising several major nonconformities.

Advantages of the process approach

The process approach:

- ♦ does not require an expert in the technology
- ♦ can be learnt by almost anyone
- ♦ focuses on results not on procedures
- ♦ can be easily verified by examination of audit reports
- ♦ creates a high degree of consistency
- ♦ adds value to the organization
- ♦ determines the effectiveness of the system
- ♦ assesses the results which the system delivers
- ♦ tests conformity with requirements that apply to more than one department
- ♦ tests linkages between departments
- ♦ tests linkages between processes
- ♦ uses realistic but challenging questions
- ♦ follows and checks the flow of work through the organization
- ♦ enables the auditee to know what the auditor is trying to establish
- ♦ obliges the auditor to look at the factors that will determine whether the operations are under control and that the controls are effective
- ♦ allows judgement to be made on the significance of the findings
- ♦ allows examination in other areas to see if problems identified are deep rooted
- ♦ encourages a search for the root cause

♦ focuses on the benefits of correcting any nonconformity related to improving organizational effectiveness.

Weakness of the process approach

It requires a real change in mind set!

Summary

Auditing is like detective work. Auditors ask questions like a detective searches for clues and the evidence is there waiting to be discovered - it is just a matter of knowing what to search for and what question to use to discover it. However, the right question posed at the wrong time is just as ineffective as the wrong question posed at the right time. Stereotype lists of questions do not actually work in practice but they are useful as a training aid, conditioning the imagination of the auditor so that the right question can be recalled when needed.

Element-based auditing provides evidence that an organization has interpreted the elements of the Standard into procedures and that the procedures are being followed but not that planned results have been achieved.

Departmental-based auditing provides some evidence that the organization has interpreted the Standard into departmental responsibilities and procedures but not that planned results have been achieved.

Task-based auditing provides evidence that specific tasks have been accomplished but not that planned results have been achieved.

One reason for conducting audits is to obtain factual input for management decisions but the vast majority of audits only produce data for use in granting a certificate, for improving documentation or for enforcing conformity. They invariably do not provide data for making managerial decisions concerned with growth, technology, staff development, products and processes because these decisions are based on current performance and often all the audit reveals is current conformity, not current performance. Tasks may or may not be conducted in accordance with the procedures but what management need to know is whether the performance meets target and whether there are opportunities for improving performance by better control or breakthrough.

Clearly a more effective auditing methodology is needed - one that focuses on performance and not on conformity. There are of course many regulations with which organizations have to comply otherwise society may be harmed. Providing organizations include these regulations in their objectives and performance measures there is no reason why focusing on performance should overlook the needs of both customers and all interested parties.

This methodology is referred to as the process approach.

Chapter 3

Quality management principles

Auditing cannot be effective unless it is approached with a clear understanding of what the objective is. During the previous two decades that objective has been focused almost entirely on conformity to requirements. Auditors therefore set out to prove conformity with a set of requirements and in many cases without a thought to the results that conformity produced. In many cases auditors actually set out to prove nonconformity, making the process adversarial and of diminishing value. To many organizations, quality management systems have been synonymous with the ISO 9000 model. They created paperwork in order to get the badge on the wall. They pulled out the documentation and dusted it off before the auditor came in and put it back when the auditor departed. This perception has been reinforced by the conformity approach. The fear that the auditor would find nonconformity led organizations to write less and less in the hope that they could not be committed to actions they had not prescribed. Had auditors approached audits rather differently, quality management systems may well have been perceived as an enabler to achieve the organization's objectives. Hence with a different approach, auditors are in a powerful position to change perceptions. One way of doing this is to use the 8 principles of quality management as the basis upon which the audit is planned, conducted and reported.

Auditors are required by the Accreditation Bodies to use all three standards in the ISO 9000 family and they cannot fail to notice that ISO 9001 states that the Standard has been developed taking into consideration the Quality management principles stated in ISO 9004. It is important that auditors do not flip through the forward, introduction, scope, and normative references to get to the requirements. It is vital that auditors read and understand the significance of section 4.1 where some fundamental requirements are stated. These generic requirements that relate to the process approach are helpful in providing an overall framework in which to fit the individual elements of the Standard. These could be overlooked if the auditor focuses on elements, departments or tasks as explained in Chapter 2.

It should have been noticed by auditors that mere conformity to requirements does not result in products that satisfy customers. No matter how many rules are imposed, if the people in the organization do not behave in an appropriate manner the organization's process will not be reliable. The 8 Quality management principles are not rules. They relate more to behaviours, values and beliefs. While their application may result in requirements for people to meet, it is only when the principles are applied through the management style and become the normalized approach to managing, performing and controlling work, that results are achieved by design and not by chance.

Auditors should be assessing capability. The scope of ISO 9001 states that it applies where an organization needs to demonstrate its ability to *consistently* provide products that meet customer and applicable regulatory requirements. No assessment of capability can be undertaken without examination of the culture. Auditors cannot acquire confidence in the organization's ability to consistently provide products that meet customer requirements unless they look beyond conformity. What the auditor finds in conformity today should not be a random occurrence but the product of a culture that will produce the same result tomorrow and the next day. Only organizations that have a set of shared values achieve this level of performance. Hence the importance of the auditor's understanding of the Quality management principles and ability to relate the application or lack of application of these principles to the findings.

These principles are not specific requirements of ISO 9001, but their application is an important contributor to the organizations ability to consistently provide acceptable product and achieve its objectives. The principles should not be viewed as 8 independent principles. They interrelate and support one another and should be viewed and applied as a coherent set.

It is also important to understand that conformity is applied within the context of seeking continual improvement. Slavishly following procedure without regard to the output is ineffective.

In Chapters 5 & 6 we show how the principles link with the questions but firstly an understanding of the principles is needed in the context of how they influence the approach taken by auditors.

Customer focus

The Customer focus principle is explained as follows:

Organizations depend on their customers and therefore should understand current and future customer needs, should meet customer requirements and strive to exceed customer expectations.

The purpose of any organization is to create and retain customers for without them they will not survive. This fundamental truth is expressed in clause 0.1 of ISO 9004. In this context customers are any organization or person that receives a product and include clients, purchasers, end-users, retailers and beneficiaries (ISO 9000 clause 3.3.5). All organizations depend on their customers. Throughout the organization the auditor should therefore expect to find that people know how vital it is to satisfy the customers and perhaps who the customers are.

To expedite particular orders the organization has to understand current customer needs. For example - a customer orders a product not realizing there are several versions. The sales person asks what the product will be used for, explains the different versions and allows the customer to choose the product that fulfils the need, adding further explanation to remove any misunderstanding. The auditor should therefore expect to find a friendly and helpful attitude in those taking orders. A behaviour that results in the customer being pleased with the way their enquiry has been dealt with is one that applies the customer focus principle.

In order to be in a position to offer products and services that meet customer needs, the organization has to conduct research to discover what customers' future needs are likely to be. The research needs to be linked with product development so that products come on stream when customers are looking for new benefits that the organization's products can satisfy. The auditor should therefore be looking for processes that explore the market, customer/consumer behaviours, potential legislation etc and that these link with the product realization processes.

Customer focus in practice means that everyone in the organization views the customer as the paymaster and therefore meeting customer requirements has priority over every other demand. However, there are other requirements that the organization has to meet that should be balanced with those of the customer which in some cases may mean that the customer cannot be satisfied without breaking the law! The organization always has a choice not to deal with certain people or organizations. The auditor should therefore expect to find a vibrant culture where the customer features at the top of a list of priorities, and in decision-making the customer's requirements are given due priority, that when dealing with customer feedback the recipient puts the customer's interests first and that everyone listens to the customer.

Customer Focus is a principle that has a clause in ISO 9001 dedicated to it. On detecting any negative traits in the culture, the auditor should ascertain how such traits serve customer satisfaction through examining the customer related processes and how effectiveness of these is measured, eg customer perception and feedback (Factual Approach), employee opinion on how customer focused the organization is (Involvement of People).

Leadership

The Leadership principle is explained as follows:

Leaders establish unity of purpose and direction of the organization. They should create and maintain the internal environment in which people can become fully involved in achieving the organization's objectives.

Unity of purpose is a state in which everyone in the organization knows why the organization exists - they share the same purpose. Effective leaders bring about this unity of purpose through the manner in which they communicate both formally and informally. This principle is expressed in ISO 9001 through the requirement for a quality policy to be established, communicated and understood. The auditor should therefore be looking for evidence that people know why they are doing things - what purpose their actions and decisions serve and how they relate to the purpose of the organization. An often-used approach is *policy deployment* through the levels of the organization where each level has the opportunity to understand and modify as necessary clarity of purpose and unity of direction.

Unity of direction is when everyone pulls in the same direction. They share common goals and objectives. ISO 9001 expresses this principle through the requirement for quality objectives to be established at relevant functions and levels within the organization. It also means that leaders constantly re-examine the direction in which they are leading the organization and make adjustments that keep the organization focused on its purpose. The auditor should therefore be looking for evidence that people know what their objectives are, what measures are employed to indicate achievement and what targets are used to measure performance. The auditor should also look for evidence that these objectives are regularly reviewed and changed as necessary to keep the organization on course.

Effective leaders motivate people to achieve their objectives and the means of motivating people is to create an environment in which the needs of people are respected, their efforts rewarded and their contribution encouraged. This principle is expressed in ISO 9001 through the requirement for the work environment to be determined and managed. ISO 9000 defines work environment as a set of conditions under which work is performed. It explains that these conditions include physical, social, psychological and environmental factors. The auditor should look at the human factors that affect the work environment as well as looking at the physical conditions of work areas to establish that an adequate needs analysis has been performed and the recommendations implemented. In doing so the auditor should ascertain that management has created conditions in which people are motivated to achieve the organization's objectives. Questions posed to those in the work area may reveal whether they are motivated. While evidence from one person may not indicate a problem, it depends on whom that person is. If they manage a number of staff there may be a leadership problem if this person claims to be less than satisfied with the working conditions. If evidence reveals that many people are not motivated by the working conditions, this too reveals a leadership problem. Once again the auditor should ascertain whether management is aware of this, (perhaps from employee feedback using the Factual approach principle) and what action has been taken to prevent this having a negative effect on conformity to product requirements.

Leadership itself is not a requirement of ISO 9001 but there are several requirements, as shown above, that apply this principle. When the evidence from asking these questions is evaluated, the auditor should be able to conclude whether or not the organization is applying the leadership principle.

Involvement of people

The Involvement of people principle is explained as follows:

People at all levels are the essence of an organization and their full involvement enables their abilities to be used for the organization's benefit.

An organization is a group of people that is formed for a particular purpose. Without the people the organization does not exist, hence why this principle makes the claim that people are the essence of an organization. People are not machines and when treated as such become dissatisfied, unproductive, ineffective and de-motivated and are unlikely to fulfil the organization's objectives. Involving people in matters that affect what they do and how they do it will lead to improved productivity. The people doing the job are more likely than anyone else to know what is preventing successful achievement of their objectives than anyone else. Unlike machines people have unlimited imagination, perform many roles both in an outside the work environment and freely acquire knowledge and experience without being instructed to do so. Employers can never employ only part of a person; they either take the whole person or none at all. In all organizations there is often untapped potential in its people that given the right conditions can make a difference between success and failure.

The auditor should look at the way decisions are made, who is involved and whether those affected by them are being consulted. The way responsibilities are assigned and authority delegated indicates whether the organization trusts its people (the **Leadership principle**) and while there is no requirement in ISO 9001 requiring people to be involved, there are several clauses that can be seen to apply this principle when interpreted in this context.

The requirement in clause 4.1 for the organization to continually improve the effectiveness of the system cannot be met without involving the people. As stated previously people are not machines, so must be involved if effectiveness is to improve.

The requirement in clause 5.1 for top management to communicate the importance of meeting customer as well as statutory and regulatory requirements cannot be met without involving people. Effective communication consists of four steps; attention, understanding, acceptance and action. It is not just the sending of messages from one source to another.

The requirement in clause 5.3 for the quality policy to be communicated and understood cannot be met without involving people.

The requirement in clause 5.5.1 for responsibilities and authority to be communicated also cannot be met without involving people. The management representative cannot obtain the information needed to report on the performance of the system as required by clause 5.5.2 unless people are involved and contribute. Also in this clause, the awareness of customer requirements cannot be promoted throughout the organization without the involvement of people.

Communication features again in clause 5.5.3. This requires communication processes to be established (the **Process** approach principle) and this requirement cannot be met without involving people.

Although the involvement of people is itself not a requirement, there are many requirements that cannot be met without involving people.

Process approach

The Process approach principle is explained as follows:

A desired result is achieved more effectively when activities and related resources are managed as a process.

This principle clearly explains that processes achieve results and behind every result is a process. Processes combine activities, physical, financial and human resources (including behaviours) to achieve results. All results (good or bad) are produced from processes but in many cases, the process is not managed and the outcome is the result of chance and not design. When the process of achieving results is designed and managed effectively, the outcomes become predictable.

The essence of the process approach is stated in clause 0.2 of ISO 9001 and translated into requirements in clause 4.1 with one exception. There is no mention of needs, objectives and requirements but this is addressed in sections 5 and 7 of ISO 9001. ISO 9001 includes a model of a process-based quality management system but it is symbolic and not intended to represent any particular system. In fact the measurement, analysis and improvement box being shown off-line rather than in-line between customer requirement and customer satisfaction, does give the impression that measurements are not concerned with product. The Standard is structured for ease of reading and to accommodate requirements from the previous version rather than strict adherence to a process approach. This somewhat unique structure may mislead auditors into thinking that the requirements reflect application of the process approach and therefore by confirming compliance with these requirements, an organization must be applying the process approach. There are other more relevant examples of the process approach in the family of standards. ISO 9000 clause 2.3 shows an 8-step general approach, clause 2.6 shows how top management uses the process approach and clause 2.9 shows how the process approach can be applied to achieve continual improvement.

After studying the family of standards and particularly clause 4.1 of ISO 9001 the auditor should have a clear idea of what the process approach is about and the set of factors that make it distinguishable from other approaches. By focussing on results rather than tasks, the auditor is more able to establish whether the organization is managing its processes as required by clause 4.1 of ISO 9001. The auditor should look at the objectives the organization desires to achieve and examine the process by which these objectives are achieved. This will take the auditor from top to bottom in the organization and across organizational boundaries.

System approach to management

The Systems approach principle is explained as follows:

Identifying, understanding and managing interrelated processes as a system contributes to the organization's effectiveness and efficiency in achieving its objectives.

A system is a set of interconnected processes that achieve specific objectives; therefore identifying the processes that comprise the system is critical to its effectiveness. When the processes in an organization are not formed into a coherent system, there will be disconnections and the outputs of one process will not match with the input requirements of other processes. In practice, people compensate for these inadequacies and it appears to top management that operations are running smoothly. When re-organizations re-deploy the people, the informal practices are no longer applied and performance declines. When processes are interconnected so that the outputs of one process match the input requirements of other processes, there is no need for informal practices and re-organizations should have no effect on performance. Hence the purpose behind creating a coherent system is to improve efficiency and effectiveness of the organization.

The concept that results are achieved through processes and that systems are sets of interconnected processes leads to the conclusion that system documentation is merely a vehicle for defining and communicating information and is not itself the system as so many have perceived it to be. When auditors look at the system, they are therefore not looking at a set of documents but a dynamic enabler through which the organization produces its output. Looking at a system means looking at the processes, the human, physical and financial resources, the information, the results that the system generates and the feedback loops that cause improvement.

The auditor should therefore look at the organization's objectives and establish that a set of interconnected processes has been identified. By looking at the boundaries between processes the auditor can also establish whether the links between outputs and inputs are matched. Any disconnections indicate that clause 4.1b) is not adequately implemented. A key requirement is for the maintenance of system integrity (clause 5.4.2b) so the auditor should be looking at the way changes are made to products, processes, the organization and the working environment; probably by examining the change management process.

Continual improvement

The Continual improvement principle is explained as follows:

Continual improvement of the organization's overall performance should be a permanent objective of the organization.

Improvement means a beneficial change and continual improvement means recurring beneficial change. The beneficial change that this principle focuses on is the organization's overall performance - this means the organization's performance with respect to its customers, its people, society and its investors. There is no mention in this explanation about product quality. This is only one aspect of performance. However, ISO 9001 in reference to continual improvement frequently refers to continually improving the effectiveness of the quality management system i.e. that one of the key outputs from the QMS is product quality.

There is a requirement in clause 5.1 for top management to demonstrate its commitment to continual improvement. The auditor should be looking for policy, objectives, processes, resources and results that relate to continual improvement and the involvement of top management in all these aspects.

The auditor should be looking at processes to establish that there are review and improvement mechanisms that examine performance and identify opportunities for improvement. The auditor should also find everyone having a responsibility to improve the performance of the activities or processes for which they are responsible and having the skills, competence and opportunity to do it. From the way people behave, the auditor should observe that they continually look for better ways of doing things. When looking at processes and the results they deliver, the auditor should observe that both targets and results improve over time, indicating that the organization is applying the continual improvement principle.

Factual approach to decision making

The Factual approach principle is explained as follows:

Effective decisions are based on the analysis of data and information.

Decisions are often made using a combination of fact, hearsay, opinion and gut feel. This principle clearly recognizes that effective decisions result from analysis of data and information where information is meaningful data and data is simply facts and figures. The requirements of ISO 9001 apply this principle in several ways. The general requirement for records to be established and maintained in clause 4.2.4 when linked to the monitoring, measurement and analysis requirements of clauses 4.1, 8.2 and 8.4 clearly show application of this principle. As the system is the means by which the organization achieves its objectives, there are no decisions that fall outside the system and therefore the system should either generate or capture all the facts needed to make decisions.

The auditor should look at the way decisions are made and this will be revealed from an examination of records and reports. All decisions that affect achievement of the organization's objectives should be based upon defined criteria as required by clause 4.1c) of ISO 9001. Those making the decisions should be authorised to do so as required by clause 5.5.1. The auditor can request sight of the data and information used to make the decisions so that the auditee can show that the decisions were based on facts that demonstrate that the criteria was or was not met.

Mutually beneficial supplier relationships

The Mutually beneficial supplier relationships principle is explained as follows:

An organization and its suppliers are interdependent and a mutually beneficial relationship enhances the ability of both to create value.

Over the last 100 years the market for goods and services has changed dramatically. Prior to the 1920s most firms focused on production in the belief that a quality product will sell itself. From the 1920s to the 1950s, many firms focused on selling what they could make regardless of whether the customer actually needed it. From the 1950s to the 1990s the market turned around from a seller's market to a buyers market as customers became more discerning and firms began to focus on identifying customer needs and producing products and services that satisfied these needs. During the last 10 years, customer orientation has been taken one step further by focusing on establishing and maintaining relationships with both customers and suppliers. From a simple exchange between buyer and seller, there evolved strategic alliances and partnerships that cut inventory, packaging and most importantly cut the costs of acquiring new customers and suppliers. There is a net benefit to both parties. For the customer, the supplier is more inclined to keep its promises as the relationship secures future orders. There is more empathy - the customer sees the supplier's point of view and vice versa. There is more give and take that binds the two organizations closer together and ultimately there is trust that holds the partnership together. Absent will be adversarial relationships and one-off transactions when either party can walk away from the deal. The partnerships will also encourage better after sales care and more customer focus throughout the organization (everyone knows their customers as there are fewer of them).

Partnerships are not appropriate in all situations but this does not mean that the way an organization deals with its suppliers and its customers should not be mutually beneficial. The last 100 years provide ample evidence of the negative effects of the production era and the seller's era where both customers and suppliers were treated as adversaries.

There are no specific requirements in ISO 9001 that apply this principle. However, there are a number of requirements that relate to the effective management of supplier relationships. By applying the process approach to supply management, the organization will set objectives and measures, establish supply processes, review and improve performance and seek better ways of achieving both organization and supplier objectives – one of which might be the formation of partnerships. More specifically, the selection and evaluation of suppliers requires consideration of relationships and setting of review criteria.

The auditor should look for factors that act as barriers to mutual beneficial relationships on the grounds that negative factors serve to cause nonconformity. Hence an organization that seeks to form mutually beneficial relationships is taking preventive action as required by ISO 9001.

Chapter 4

The process approach

The questions that auditors ask when using the conformity approach have been driven from the cliché:

Say what you do

Do what you say

Prove it

This has resulted in questions that focus on the organization's documentation so that what the auditor asks is:

Have you got a procedure for ******?

Can I see it?

Can you tell me what you do?

Where does it say that you are supposed to do ******?

Can you show me where you have ******?

The process approach is fundamentally different. The focus is on results and outcomes not on whether people have done what they said they would do. The reason for this is quite simple.

While honesty and commitment (doing what you say you will do, keeping promises etc) are important, they only achieve the results required if what people say they will do is what they should and if the results are in fact those that are needed. This leads to the first question:

> *What are you trying to do?*

The question focuses on the very essence of work. All work has a purpose, all organizations have a purpose and all processes have a purpose. Constancy of purpose throughout the organization is key to its survival. People can get so tied up in today's problems that they forget what they were originally trying to do. At the upper level it is the reason for existing, the mission. At the intermediate level it is meeting objectives and targets and at the lower level it is about accomplishing a task. Underlying the purpose, mission or objectives is something else that has more to do with *what we are not trying to do.* "We are trying to run a railroad, but we not in the business of exploiting our employees, deceiving our customers or damaging the environment". These are often referred to as values and give the organization a character of its own. There are also other influencing factors that set boundary conditions for what an organization does and the manner in which it decides to do it - the markets it is in, the products it chooses to develop, the things it decides it will not do. These are often referred to as policies and it is these values and policies that guide the organization on its journey and are bound up in the expression of what it is trying to do.

Having established what the organization is trying to do, it follows that the auditor should establish whether there is a system, a process or a method in place that will achieve this objective. This leads to the second question:

> ## How do you make it happen?

Purpose, mission, values, policies, objectives and targets become slogans without a system, a process or a method in place to achieve them. No goal should be set without describing how it is to be accomplished. To make it happen the organization may build a new factory, set up a new organization, design a new system, launch a new project or develop new products, processes, materials, methods or procedures. The scale of work will depend on what the organization, the process or the person is trying to do.

As the process approach is focused on results, it follows that the auditor should establish that the organization knows whether the desired results are being achieved. This leads us to the third question:

> ## How do you know it's right?

At the upper level, this question is not addressed at an individual but at the organization and hence questions whether the top management know how the organization is performing against the plan. At the intermediate level, the question addresses how the process is performing against the process objectives, and at the lower level, it addresses how the individual is performing against work assignments or objectives. Such knowledge is provided in many ways. For the operator it may come from an instrument panel on a machine and is immediate. For the manager it may come from observation and reports and may be immediate but more than likely it will be hours/days old. For the CEO it will come from financial and other information and will be months old depending on the business cycle. In some service organizations it is possible for the CEO to have direct access to performance indicators in their office such as the number of calls waiting in a call centre, system availability in a data centre and power generation levels in a power station. For many, such technology is not yet so sophisticated and management has to rely on reports of events that have already happened.

There are many ways in which results can be achieved. Some are effective and others not so effective. All organizations need to avoid loss otherwise they will not survive and for many this has resulted in an obsession with profits. Profits result from what the organization does and are therefore affected by the efficiency and effectiveness of its operations. If the organization has no control over its operations, the profits will be erratic - some months they will be in the black - other months they will be in the red. Even when controls stabilize the quality of the outputs, the methods used may not be the best that could be used. ISO 9000 requires continual improvement that should not only be interpreted as improving the quality of the output, but improving the effectiveness by which the output is generated. This leads us to the third question:

> *How do you know it's the best way of doing it?*

An organization that never questions how it does things, never questions the rules, the policies, is unlikely to progress and will inevitably be overtaken by the competition. It is an organization in which the auditor might hear "We have always done it this way." or "It's more than my job's worth to question the rules." The rules, the procedures, may once have been the best thing to do but things change. The environment in which the organization operates change, the economic and market forces change and hence, it is wise to question whether we are doing things in the right way - those organization that do, are innovative and as a result continually improve. In any situation it is unlikely that there is only one way of doing something, What may appear to be an unacceptable way in one situation may turn out to be an acceptable way in another - it all depends on the context. However, within a certain context, there are likely to be more/less effective ways of doing things. If an organization is to sustain its performance it needs to continually look for better ways. Competition often shows up the weaknesses in an organization and forces organizations to find better ways of doing things, which ultimately will lead to more satisfied customers. Organizations that have no idea whether the way they do things is good or bad practice are operating in a vacuum and are missing great opportunities for improvement.

Even after confirming that the organization knows what it is trying to do, has a system to achieve it, knows it is doing it right and is using the best ways of doing it, there remains one vital issue upon which the survival of the enterprise depends. It has to be doing the right things for it to be profitable and satisfy the needs and expectations of the customer and other interested parties. This lead to the final question:

How do you know it's the right thing to do?

An organization that never questions whether it is doing the right things, never questions the objectives or the requirements is unlikely to fulfil its purpose/mission and will inevitably be overtaken by the competition. It is an organization in which the auditor might hear "If this wasn't the right thing to do, our customers would complain". or "We have always measured customer satisfaction by the number of written complaints received." The objectives may once have been the right thing to achieve but things have changed and the objective or the way it is measured is not longer relevant to achieving our purpose. E.g. customers weren't feeding back poor performance because they had moved to the competition. Customer satisfaction appeared high because no written complaints had been received but verbal dissatisfaction was high.

It is therefore vital that an organization regularly reviews its objectives and how those objectives are measured to ensure they remain relevant to the fulfilment of the purpose/mission.

These are the 5 key questions that will establish whether the organization has the capability of fulfilling the purpose for which it was created. That purpose is of no concern to the auditor, but in examining an organization, purpose is the one factor that drives everything within it.

Clearly an auditor will need to ask more than 5 questions and for each of the five, there are several other questions that need to be asked to reveal whether the organization is being managed in the most effective way.

One might argue that ISO 9001 is not concerned with whether the organization is being managed effectively but if an organization is not being managed effectively it clearly will not be able to *demonstrate its ability to consistently provide product that meets customer and applicable regulatory requirements and enhance customer satisfaction through the effective application of the system (ISO 9001 clause 1.1).* This is the stated purpose of ISO 9001 and hence the basis for advocating that organizations need to be able to answer these 5 key questions.

Q1 What are you trying to do?

Q2 How do you make it happen?

Q3 How do you know it's right?

Q4 How do you know it's the best way of doing it?

Q5 How do you know it's the right thing to do?

There are basically three levels in any organization:

♦ The Enterprise level where the focus is on Strategy and where the results are expressed in terms of fulfilling the mission

♦ The Management level where the focus is on Customers and where the results are expressed in terms of achievement of requirements

♦ The Operational level where the focus is on Work and results are expressed in terms of delivery of outputs.

The basic questions are the same regardless of the level, but what the auditor *looks at* needs to be different and the evidence the auditor *looks for* is also different. ISO 9001 is structured in a way that results in the same question asked at different levels applying to different requirements - hence the questions are grouped together in the three levels. Applying the process approach to auditing means that the auditor uses these questions not only at each level but at every stage where a result is to be achieved, whether the stage is the organization as a whole, a business process within the organization, a work process within a business process, a task within a work process or an activity that forms part of a task. The result may be a product supplied to an external customer, a component supplied to an internal department or information supplied to a process or to another person.

In Chapter 8 these questions are applied to several business processes and sub-processes. These are simply models. They do not reflect any particular organization. While the way an organization is structured should not affect the processes required to achieve its objectives, the labels attributed to these processes vary. A marketing process in one organization is a sales process in another. They are included in the book by way of examples in order to promote understanding of the approach taken. There are some generic questions and some specific questions. In the next three Chapters we will take each generic question at the Enterprise, Managerial and Operational levels and explain the other questions that need to be asked. We will explain why they need to be asked, how they relate to ISO 9001 and what evidence they should generate. Many requirements in ISO 9001 are detail requirements that would be explored by the auditor probing the response or the evidence presented. Although the questions may appear to follow in a sequence, there is no right or wrong sequence in which these questions should be asked. For instance it may be appropriate to ask questions about results after being shown the objectives rather than leave the questions until the processes have been examined. We will also explain the terminology used. Unfortunately there is no universal understanding and application of management terms. A policy to one organization might be an objective to another; a plan is a strategy at one level and a procedure at another. A term is merely a label given to a concept and while the concepts are universal the labels given to them are not. In reading this book we ask that you accept the meanings that we have defined.

Chapter 5

Questions at the enterprise level

Q1   What are you trying to do?

The question is aimed at establishing whether the reason for doing things is understood, because if people do not know what they are trying to do, any result will be acceptable!

At the Enterprise level the question to ask is:

> *What is the purpose/mission of the organization?*

The link between an organization's purpose and the management system is stated in ISO 9001 clause 5.3 where it requires the quality policy to be appropriate to the purpose of the organization. Clearly unless the purpose is known, the auditor cannot determine whether the policy is appropriate.

> **Purpose**
> The reason for existing

The purpose of an organization is the reason for which it was created - why it does what it does. Statements of purpose at the enterprise level can be expressed in **purpose** or **mission** statements. The mission of an organization is the journey it is taking and clearly an organization could have been established simply to undertake a particular journey or do a particular thing that gives it a reason for existence.

> **Mission**
> The overall direction in which the organization is going

> *What analysis has been carried out to determine the critical factors that affect accomplishment of the purpose/mission?*

Although ISO 9001 requires the policy to be appropriate to the purpose of the organization and to provide a framework for establishing objectives, in reality it is not a question of fixing the words so that there is a linkage. The purpose in establishing policy and objectives is to drive the organization towards accomplishing its mission or fulfilling its purpose. Therefore some analysis is needed to identify the factors that affect success and thus identify the subjects that need to be controlled by the organization. From an awareness of these factors the most appropriate policy and objectives will be derived.

> ## *How were these factors identified and evaluated?*

The auditor needs to establish that the policy and objectives are not merely plucked out of the air or copied from someone else, but developed out of an analysis of the factors that affect the organization's success. If this is done there is a good chance that the organization will willingly commit to the policy and objectives. If it borrows the policy and objectives from someone else, it will merely pay lip service to them. The policy should result from the analysis.

> ## *What policies have been established to guide the organization in accomplishing its purpose/mission?*

This concept was supposed to be applied by requiring organizations to declare their Quality Policy but as neither the auditors nor the managers understood what the term *Quality Policy* meant, it resulted in auditors asking "Can you tell me what the Quality Policy is?"

Clearly, knowing of the quality policy, will not demonstrate whether it is understood or applied. Neither will it establish that the organization understands the manner in which its results need to be achieved to satisfy the interested parties. It is in this context that ISO 9000:2000 differs significantly from ISO 9000:1994. There remains the requirement for the organization to establish a quality policy and a new requirement for it to be demonstrated.

The term *policy* is used in many different ways. In ISO 9000 it states that the "quality policy is overall intentions and direction of an organization related to quality as formally expressed by top management". In other words *policy* guides organizations to achieve their goals and is often expressed by top management as *corporate policy*.. Other policies will be expressed at different levels in the organization. However, it is not enough for organizations to achieve results. The proof is not in whether people have done what they say, but in whether the results have been achieved in a manner that satisfies the interested parties.

Achieving results without consideration of the interested parties is taking a selfish approach to management, an autocratic, an unethical or immoral approach. None of us live in a vacuum. We all depend on one another. If we are to survive in our society, we must take into consideration how what we do affects others. This means we need to have shared values that condition our behaviour and in the context of ISO 9000 and quality policy, this is what the quality policy should represent. Further proof is provided in ISO 9000 where it states that the Quality management principles presented in the Standard can form the basis for the establishment of a quality policy. The 2nd Quality management principle is *Leadership* and this is about establishing unity of purpose and direction and creating an environment in which people can become fully involved in achieving the organization's objectives. One of the instruments used by leaders to carry out their role is *policy*. Whether the organization calls such a statement a policy, a quality policy or a vision and values statement is not important. The auditor should seek evidence that the factors that will condition the manner in which people will perform their actions and take decision have been defined, using the 8 Quality management principles as a guide to judge whether these statements are in line with the intent of the standard.

> **Leadership**
> Leaders establish unity of purpose and direction for the organization.

> **Policy**
> A set of values and rules that are intended to guide the actions (behaviours) and decisions of those they affect

The policies result from a process that should have involved an analysis of the factors that affect the organization's success.

What is the process by which policies are established?

All work is accomplished through a process and therefore *policy* is created through a process. If there is a process in place it means that management is serious about wanting the policy to be the right policy. By applying the process approach to this policy-setting process we are seeking answers to two further questions, "How do you make it happen and how do you know it's right?"

In the context of policy, making policy happen is concerned with its communication.

> ## *How are the organization's policies communicated throughout the organization?*

This is a requirement of ISO 9001 clause 5.3d. But communication is more than sending out messages, it is about understanding and here the Standard also requires the quality policy to be understood.

> ## *How have those responsible for implementing these policies been involved in their development?*

Clearly if those concerned have not been involved in the development of policies they are less likely to understand their importance. Involvement of people is one of the 8 Quality management principles and hence is addressed by this question.

There needs to be some measures to test understanding - indicators that will signal whether the policy has reached the right people.

> ## *What measures are used to indicate successful implementation of these policies?*

If one of the factors that was critical to the organization's success was *keeping a focus on customers* it may have a Customer Focus policy that looks like this:

We will listen to our customers, understand and balance their needs and expectations with those of our suppliers, employees, investors and society and endeavour to give full satisfaction to all parties.

So how will management know whether this policy is understood? What measures will be used to test understanding? Some measures might be:

- ♦ Customer complaints
- ♦ Employee complaints
- ♦ Supplier complaints
- ♦ Complaints from investors

♦　Complaints from the community

Having established measures, the organization obviously needs to apply them.

How is understanding of these policies confirmed?

ISO 9001 clause 5.1b requires top management to demonstrate commitment to the QMS by establishing a quality policy. Policy is not established by issuing a document. It has to be lived by the people in the organization. Management therefore needs to confirm that its policy is understood. Using the measures such as those above, the auditor should expect that the complaints have not only been examined and resolved but that the root cause has been established for signs that the policy has not been understood.

At the Enterprise level, the question 'What you are trying to do?' is very fundamental to the direction in which the organization is going. Knowing where the organization is going is vital to its survival. But as Deming remarks[1], "Goals without a plan for accomplishing them become mere slogans and useless. They generate frustration and resentment." Therefore, the next step is for the auditor to establish if the organization has a plan in place to make it happen.....

---

[1] Deming Management Method by Mary Walton 1986

Q2   How do you make it happen?

At the Enterprise level, making things happen is achieved though strategic planning, setting objectives and targets. These are deployed through the organization, as the results personnel are required to achieve. As the process approach is focused on results not on tasks, the auditor needs to examine the process by which the organization's objectives are established. These series of questions therefore relate to the strategy the organization has developed to accomplish its goals.

> **Strategy**
> The overall approach for achieving objectives

> *What are the key stages in the process used to establish the objectives and processes for achieving the organization's goals?*

The answer to this question will set the scene for exploring the process. Depending on the type and nature of the organization, there may be a strategic planning process, a business planning process, or simply a budgeting process. Whatever the organization calls this process there are some key facts that need to be discovered.

> *What analysis has been carried out to understand the organization's current performance and the current and future needs and expectations of all interested parties?*

ISO 9001 requires that top management ensures that customer requirements are determined. ISO 9000 defines 'requirements' as needs or expectations that are stated, generally implied or obligatory. Here the Standard is not addressing the situation when a customer places an order - that is dealt with in clause 7.2.1. It is addressing the implementation of policy whereby the organization will have declared a commitment to comply with requirements. Clearly it can't do this if it has not set out to discover what these requirements are likely to be. It is too late when a customer places an order to discover that products and services need to exhibit certain features or that certain regulations have to be met. If you wait until the customer places the order, you will simply not be able to deliver. All organizations therefore need to understand current and future customer needs and expectations and this is substantiated by the Customer focus principle. Therefore any organization that is committed to meeting ISO 9000 would need to analyse its performance and establish what its potential customers and regulators require. The analysis needs to be robust and not a superficial review. The auditor therefore needs to explore the soundness of the analysis.

> *What research was carried out to validate these factors?*

A considered answer will indicate that the organization takes this research seriously but having done the research it is not a 'one off' event. Customer needs keep changing.

> *How do you maintain the integrity of the results of this research?*

This question aims to discover whether the organization periodically reviews the results of the research and repeats it to keep the data current (a requirement of ISO 9001 clause 4.2.3b) and also whether the organization keeps the information under control thus complying with the other requirements of clause 4.2.3.

> **Customer focus**
> Organizations depend on their customers and therefore should understand current and future customer needs, should meet customer requirements and strive to exceed customer expectations.

An outcome from the analysis should be the identification of any regulations that apply to the business and its products and service.

> *What are the relevant statutory and regulator requirements that impact the mission?*

It is of no concern to the system auditor whether the list of regulations is complete, but whether the organization used a soundly based process to determine them. The analysis is carried out for one purpose - to determine what the organization aims to achieve currently and in the future.

> *What objectives have been established as a result of this research to enable the organization to achieve its purpose/mission?*

Merely asking what the quality objectives are and being shown a document listing them will not demonstrate they are appropriate to the organization or as required by ISO 9001, "*consistent with the quality policy*". At the Enterprise level these objectives may be divided into categories such as Customers, People, Society and Performance. A comprehensive list of measures is given in the guidance on the European Excellence Model. Key objectives relative to ISO 9001 would address the 8 Quality management principles in one form or another. For example the analysis of regulations may have revealed that the organization needs to reduce pollution levels and therefore the auditor should ask what objectives have been established to comply with the regulation.

It is relatively easy to pick one objective off at a time, but in reality, there will be priorities. Not all objectives will have the same priority.

> *What analysis has been carried out to balance these objectives and set priorities for action?*

There will be objectives focused on customers but others on employees, on society etc and they need to be balanced.

The objectives will impact the organization in many ways but those that will have most impact will be concerned with new products and services and with abandoning existing products and services. There will also be objectives that deal with specific initiatives such as seeking ISO 9000 certification or the Business Excellence Award.

> *What products, services, markets and projects are necessary to achieve these objectives?*

The answers to this question will establish whether the current offerings will deliver the organization's objectives. They should also identify whether any new offerings are required or whether any need to be abandoned.

> *Which products, services, markets, projects need to be abandoned, as they do not fulfil these objectives?*

The objectives that emerge from the analysis of customer needs and expectations become requirements that the organization needs to meet. Failure to meet these requirements will result in dissatisfied customers. According to

ISO 9000, a failure to meet a requirement is termed *nonconformity* and preventive action is that taken to prevent the occurrence of nonconformity.

> ### How are the risks to achieving these objectives identified and evaluated?

Risk assessment is a preventive action technique and thus implements the requirements of clause 8.5.3 of ISO 9001. In asking how risks are identified the organization responds to clause 8.5.3a and asking how they are managed a response to clauses 8.5.3b) to e) can be explored. For example if an objective of the organization is to achieve 100% on-time delivery, the auditor should ask whether an analysis of the risks to achieve this has been determined and what actions the organization have decided to take to minimise them. Another technique is to use Failure Modes Effects Analysis or What if? - analysis to identify potential risks to success. The auditor could therefore ask whether the modes of failure have been identified and what action has been taken as a result.

It is only after an understanding of the organization's objectives has been acquired that the auditor can move on to exploring the processes to achieve them.

> ### What set of interconnected processes have been established to deliver the required products and services to customers?

At the Enterprise level, these processes are the 'business' processes rather than the 'work' processes and certainly not the procedures. They are also not functions or departments and if necessary the auditor needs to establish that the organization understands how processes differ from functions, departments and procedures. The identity of processes is addressed by clause 4.1a) of ISO 9001 and their interaction by clause 4.1b). The 5th

> **System approach to management**
> Identifying and managing interrelated processes as a system contributes to the organization's effectiveness and efficiency in achieving its objectives.

principle of quality management is the **System approach to management** and by asking for a set of interconnected processes the auditor is seeking to establish that the organization has established a **system**. Although the terms 'interrelated' and 'interacting' are used in the definitions, processes cannot interact unless they are connected. It would be a leading question to ask what *system* has been established, as the organization may perceive a system as a set of documents!

While the core processes to develop and supply product will probably have been established some time ago, the objectives for new products and services may impact

System
A set of interconnected processes for achieving a specific objective.

these processes such that modification is needed. Processes designed for one set of conditions may not be capable of meeting new conditions. If new technology is needed, the auditor should ask what changes to these processes have been agreed to introduce the new technology. If 100% on-time delivery is an objective, the auditor should ask what changes to the existing processes have been agreed to improve delivery performance. In order to make things happen, the organization may need to devise improvement plans for existing processes to enhance their performance.

Processes are the means to achieve objectives - some objectives will be for change and some for maintaining the status quo. Of those focused on change there will be some that drive the creation of new or modified products and services and those that serve to eliminate products and services that have reached the end of their life cycle.

> ### *What processes have been established to withdraw obsolete products & services and to abandon projects?*

In the question is a reference to 'projects'. A project is an undertaking that serves to accomplish a specific objective that is part of a greater strategy. Once the objective has been achieved the project is complete. When the organization's objectives for the next business

Project
A scheduled undertaking to achieve specific objectives within defined time and cost constraints.

cycle have been set, current projects need to be assessed for their relevance and abandoned if found no longer relevant to the organization's objectives. Understanding of the organizations objectives is therefore vital for the auditor to perform effectively.

Processes transform inputs into outputs of added value through use of human, physical and financial

Process
A set of interrelated tasks, behaviours and resources that achieve a result.

resources. Unless the organization has access to the necessary resources, it will not be able to achieve its objectives and will consequently not be able to satisfy its customers.

The forgoing relates to the organization's strategy, the identification of its primary objectives and the means to achieve them. It is now necessary to establish what organization structure has been designed to deliver this strategy, as it is the internal relationships that will determine the effectiveness with which the objectives are achieved. Organization structure covers locations, positions, roles and environment and is key to process effectiveness as processes often traverse departments as well as locations.

> *What analysis was carried out to determine the organizational structure and work environment needed to deliver these processes?*

Organizations comprise people and people relate to one another in their work environment. The way the organization is structured affects individual motivation and performance and therefore there is a link between structure, culture, work environment and performance. If the policies and objectives match and the policies are based on the 8 Quality management principles or their equivalent, the basis for the culture and work environment has been established. What the auditor is seeking by this question is whether the organization has made this connection and whether the structure reflects these policies. ISO 9001 clause 6.4 requires the work environment to be determined. Therefore, this question will reveal whether the links between process, structure and environment are sound.

> *What is the organization structure that results from this analysis?*

Merely asking to see the organization chart will not prove anything. What is important is the rationale that led to the chart being introduced. The organization is more likely to function effectively if the rationale is sound. The structure may be based on product, geography, function or process groupings or a mix of all four. However, from a process management viewpoint it is important that processes are designed and managed to produce the right output. By examining the organization structure the auditor should be able to establish whether there are any obvious weaknesses.

> ## *How have those responsible for operating the organization's processes been involved in their development?*

It is pertinent to ask how the system of interconnected process has been developed. ISO 9001 clause 4.1b requires the sequence and interaction of these processes to be determined and clause 5.1 requires top management to provide evidence of its commitment to the development of a QMS. Therefore, by revealing how the personnel responsible for operating the processes

Commitment
Doing everything that one has agreed to do.

have been involved in their development, evidence of **commitment** and the involvement of people should emerge.

For the organization structure to function effectively people need to know the results for which they are responsible and the boundaries for their jobs. This is expressed in various forms such as job/role responsibilities and authority. These may also cover key result areas and measurable output targets which should be linked to the process. Hence the auditor needs to explore how the policies, objectives and plans have been deployed throughout the structure.

> ## *How have the plans for achieving the organization's objectives been deployed within the organization?*

Clearly this is vital and is addressed in ISO 9001 clauses 5.1, 5.3, 5.5.1 and 5.5.3. At the Enterprise level the auditor needs to establish how the plans and actions to achieve the objectives are deployed throughout the organization. The organization may use various means, including the cascading of objectives or peer groups at each level to determine or confirm plans and feedback in an iterative manner. This would provide further evidence against clause 5.4.1.

> ## *How do you ensure the plans for achieving the organization's objectives are understood?*

The organization may have several ways of achieving this but the auditor is only concerned that the methods used have taken into account the recipient's needs and hence applies the Involvement of people principle. Using a method as described above would contribute to the understanding of objectives and plans. However, the auditor should establish how the cascaded objectives and plans have been translated into appropriate language and measurable outputs to which each level can respond.

> ## *How is the currency, validity and integrity of the information contained in these plans maintained?*

It is not the documents that really need to be controlled but the information they contain. ISO 9001 clause 4.2.3 addresses document control and in particular, currency is addressed by clause 4.2.3d), validity is addressed by clause 4.2.3a) and integrity by clauses 4.2.3b), c), e), f) and g).

In the past auditors have placed too much emphasis on whether documents have been correctly numbered, dated and approved. The emphasis should be on whether the organization has established what information is required by the process to achieve the objectives and how the integrity, validity and currency are maintained.

Having established how the organization's objectives are developed and communicated, the auditor can move on to establish the extent to which the objectives are being achieved.....

Q3   How do you know it's right?

Achievement needs to be measured but for this the units of measure need to be determined and the standard or target, which is to be aimed for, needs to be set. This was one problem with the Conformity Approach. Evidence was obtained that a quality policy and objectives had been defined and that everyone knew them, but there was no requirement for any measurement of achievement. ISO 9001 clause 8.2.3 requires the methods used for measuring processes to demonstrate they achieve planned results i.e. achieve objectives.

Implementation of ISO 9001:1994 has led auditors to ask for records of management reviews and after studying minutes of meetings, lists of customer complaints and audit results these auditors have concluded that the system is being reviewed. Rarely were the questions asked of how the system was contributing to the achievement of the business objectives and how it could be more effective. ISO 9001 clause 5.6.1 requires the system to be reviewed by top management for its continuing suitability, adequacy and effectiveness. Such a review is not simply an examination of complaints and audit results but a more thorough evaluation of performance, the first element of which is whether objectives are being achieved - i.e. Is the system adequate?.

> *What measures are used to verify achievement of the organization's objectives and what target values have been agreed?*

For each objective there should be measures to determine performance and targets to determine achievement. This is application of the **Factual approach** and the **Process approach** principles. An objective of achieving customer satisfaction is not measurable unless the factors that are deemed to constitute customer satisfaction are determined. ISO 9001 requires the organization to monitor information relating to customer satisfaction and hence the auditor should discover what factors the organization is employing. One measure may be timely resolution of complaints and the target value

> **Process approach**
> A desired result is achieved more efficiently when activities and related resources are managed as a process.

may be to resolve all complaints within 28 days. Another may be product delivery and the target may be to achieve 100% on time delivery. These results may appear easy enough to measure but nonetheless the way in which achievement could be measured will vary.

> ## What results are being achieved against these targets?

The auditor should establish what results are currently being achieved against each of the targets and that there is a match between what is actually being measured and what was planned to be measured.

> ## What method of measurement is used and how often are measurements taken?

Using the examples above to illustrate what the auditor should look for, the method for measuring complaint resolution would need to define what is and what is not a complaint, what constitutes *resolution* and when the 28 day period starts and ends. Similarly with 100% on-time delivery, a definition of delivery is needed. Is it the time the goods leave the factory gates? Does early delivery constitute *on-time delivery*? Is there a margin of error? What happens if the delivery would have been on-time but for a rail strike? How are these counted, who counts them and when are they counted? At the enterprise level, it is also vital that the data used to measure the performance of the organization is of the highest integrity.

> ## What methods are used to ensure the integrity of these measurements?

Use of invalid data will mislead top management and could harm the organization. This is expressed by the **Factual approach principle**. Management and auditors alike have largely ignored the importance and significance of the integrity of measurement. Previously the focus has been confined to the calibration of measuring devices that has been interpreted mainly in the manufacturing context. However, it is just as important to establish consistency and calibration of measurement in all contexts of decision-making.

> **Factual approach to decision making**
> Effective decisions are based on the analysis of data and information.

For example: What methods are used to ensure that market research results are measured in a consistent way? What methods are used to ensure that if two people assessed the competence of a colleague, they would arrive at a similar conclusion? The requirements in ISO 9001 clause 7.6 whilst focusing on measuring devices contain essential requirements that relate to <u>all</u> measurement.

> ### *How are the results of measuring business performance captured?*

Measurements of all the values need to be collected and collated, as the measurements will probably be taken at different times and at different locations in the organization. ISO 9001 clause 8.4 requires data on the effectiveness of the system to be collected. ISO 9001 clause 5.5.2 also requires the management representative to report to top management on the performance of the system and clearly this cannot be done if the data is not collected.

> ### *How are the results conveyed to those responsible for taking action?*

The auditor needs to establish not only that data for the agreed measures has been collected but also how that data has been reviewed by those responsible for taking action on the results and subsequently that investigations have been carried out.

> ### *What analysis has been performed to determine the cause in the difference between actual and planned results?*

ISO 9001 clause 8.4 requires data to be analysed as does clauses 8.5.2 and 8.5.3 on corrective and preventive action. The auditor should look for evidence that the root cause of the difference has been established when examining the evidence. At the Enterprise level, the agreed actions may well be decided at monthly meetings, board meetings or the management review. It is important that the auditor establishes not only that the actions have been agreed but also that benefits of such actions have been defined. This provides a basis on which the organization can demonstrate improvement.

> ### *What improvement in results was obtained from the last review of performance?*

The simple maxim applies - no measurement without recording, no recording without analysis and no analysis without action - and the action taken should result in improvement. ISO 9001 clause 8.4 requires the analysis to identify where continual improvement can be made. Clause 8.5.1 requires continual improvement of the system through use of the analysis of data and hence the auditor should expect to find evidence of improved performance against targets.

If an organization is to sustain its performance it needs to continually look for better ways of doing things and this is a key element of ISO 9001. In addition to a clause dedicated to continual improvement it features in management commitment (5.1) the quality policy (5.3) the provision of resources (6.1) and the analysis of data (8.4) and is the next step for the auditor to take.....

Q4   How do you know it's the best way of doing it?

The key to continual improvement is asking whether things are being done in the best possible way. An objective may be achieved but at enormous expense. This is why ISO 9001 clause 5.1 requires top management to continually improve the effectiveness of the system. Continual improvement in ISO 9000 is defined as a recurring activity to increase the ability to fulfil requirements. This naturally leads to seeking better ways of doing things. Having established a policy to guide the organization towards achieving its objectives it is therefore important that management know whether it is being implemented.

> **Continual improvement**
> Recurring activity to increase the ability to fulfil requirements.

> *What checks are used to verify that the manner in which the system is implemented is consistent with the organization's policies and values?*

ISO 9001 clause 8.2.2 requires internal audits to be conducted to determine whether the system conforms to the planned arrangements. Hence a check of the manner in which work is implemented is wholly consistent with this requirement. The organization may therefore offer its internal audit records as evidence. However, the question focuses on the policies rather than the processes and procedures, therefore unless the audits also explore the rationale behind the actions and decisions people make, valid evidence will not be revealed. Policies that express values are implemented not directly but through actions and decisions. The way managers decide to deal with staff suggestions, with staff who adhere to the rules they laid down but which result in a delayed delivery, a missed opportunity or a wasted journey are ways that indicate the manner in which the system is implemented. In other words the organization needs to demonstrate how the values are used to guide actions. How, for example, teamwork, if that was a value, was demonstrated at various levels and in various activities.

> *What results were obtained the last time these checks were performed?*

The results may be achieved and the activities implemented as planned but they may consume more than the optimum resources and take longer than necessary. This is concerned with **efficiency**, which ISO 9000 defines as the relationship between the results achieved and the resources used.

> **Efficiency**
> The relationship between the useful outputs from a process to the total input.

It is interesting to note that ISO 9000 explains the **Process** approach principle as a means to improve 'efficiency' rather than 'effectiveness'. Although ISO 9001 deliberately omits requirements for efficiency, for an organization to remain competitive and continually enhance its ability to satisfy customers and other interested parties, it needs to be efficient.

> *What checks are used to verify that the system for achieving the organization's policies and objectives is efficient?*

The question should reveal whether the organization examines its practices for better ways of doing things and examines the organization structure to find better ways of organizing people and utilizing resources. The more efficient the organization becomes, the more resources are available for allocation to productive work. As with all measurement, there needs to be criteria to judge whether the results are acceptable.

> *What are the criteria for determining whether the system is efficient?*

Productivity is a traditional measure of efficiency and the auditor can explore what criteria is used to measure the utilization of knowledge, physical resources, time and financial resources. At the Enterprise level there are likely to be some measures of productivity that are used to drive improvement efforts, allocate resources and dispose of under-utilized resources. While similar measurements will be taken within business processes, at the system level the auditor should look at the whole system for parameters that measure the system. As there is a chain of processes from identifying customers to satisfying customers, all depending upon resource management and business management, some key measures might signify system efficiency. The results should indicate whether the system is meeting the criteria for its effectiveness.

> *What results were obtained the last time these checks were performed?*

It is important that the methods employed to carry out these measurements are soundly based, as decisions affecting the organization's assets including its people will be taken on the results of the measurements. Another method is to use Benchmarking both internally and externally. By finding processes that serve similar objectives in other parts of the business or in other businesses the organization is able to rank itself again the best in a particular field.

> *What methods are used to conduct these checks and how often are they performed?*

There are benchmarking clubs, government advice centres and other ways of obtaining data that organizations can use to benchmark their processes.

It is important that people are consulted on decisions that may impact their positions in the organization and the resources they use. The concept behind the Involvement of people principle is that when people are involved they are more likely to understand how to play a more effective role in achieving the organization's objectives. ISO 9001 clause 5.6.1 requires top management to review the system to ensure its continuing suitability and it is at this review where issues of efficiency should be debated.

> *Who is involved in this assessment?*

The answer to this question also links with the policies of the organization regarding its people and by questioning system efficiency and the way it is measured, the auditor should be able to confirm whether the relevant policies are being effectively implemented. In order that any analysis of efficiency is based on facts (Factual approach principle) the results need to be recorded.

> *How are the results of this assessment captured?*

The utilization of resources is affected at all levels in the organization and improvements can often be made at the local level. However, when it comes to redeploying people, equipment, buildings and finance, these decisions are generally taken by top management and the decisions communicated to those concerned. The manner in which such information is communicated can significantly affect the outcome.

> ## How are these results conveyed to those responsible for taking action?

The auditor is not merely looking for a single method or procedure for communication. The method has to be appropriate to the message and it is these considerations that the auditor would expect to be revealed by this question. Sending a message to employees that their suggestions were rejected is unlikely to encourage them to make other suggestions. The sole purpose behind seeking to establish whether the organization is assessing the efficiency of its system is to find out if improvements are being made using soundly based methods. ISO 9001 clause 5.6.1 requires the management review to include actions related to improvement in resource needs and clearly an analysis of productivity will impact resource needs.

> ## What action was taken the last time these checks were performed that resulted in the system efficiency being improved and how was this improvement measured?

Whether the organization measures productivity or benchmarks against other organizations, it is the resulting action that is important. The auditor is not merely looking for evidence that any action has been taken - the action needs to specifically improve the efficiency of the system - it has to move the organization forward in terms of the degree of excellence in its practices.

The environment in which the organization operates changes, the economic and market forces change and therefore, management should be continually questioning whether it is doing the right things to respond to these changes. Organizations that review their objectives on a regular basis are innovative and as a result continually improve. The forgotten policy that was appropriate to a bygone age may bring its surprises when someone innocently chooses to implement it! Hence the next step for the auditor is to explore the approach taken by the organization to make sure all its policies, objectives and practices are relevant to the goals of today.....

Q5 How do you know it's the right thing to do?

Effectiveness is normally associated with doing the right things. This can mean adhering to the plan if this is the right thing to do. It can also mean achieving the target, if this is the right thing to do. ISO 9000 defines effectiveness as the extent to which planned activities are realized and planned results achieved. At the Enterprise level, doing the right things is about being in the right market with the right products of the right quality in the right location at the right time. Decisions about these things will have been made in the business planning process. A question asked previously was whether the objectives were being achieved and if so whether they were being achieved in the best way - now it is prudent to ask:

> **Effectiveness**
> The extent to which an output fulfils its purpose.

> *What checks are carried out to verify that the organization's objectives remain relevant to the achievement of its purpose/mission?*

ISO 9001 clause 5.6.1 requires the management review to assess the need for changes in the quality policy and quality objectives. This justifies why auditors should question whether a process is in place that reviews the relevance of policies and objectives. All too often the organization is slow to act and react - the world will have moved on since the original research was carried out to produce the facts that led to the objectives. Hence the auditor needs to question whether there are checks in place to test the relevance of the organization's objectives. Objectives may be set every year but may not change from year to year either because they were not met last year or because they are perceived as still being relevant. The auditor should check whether relevance is determined by perception or by fact.

> *What methods are used to conduct these checks and how often are they performed?*

At the Enterprise level, the organization should continually scan the external environment for changes that affect the organization's purpose, mission, objectives and policies, eg What are the current and future hot topics? While evidence for this may be revealed from such questions as, "What analysis has been carried out to understand the organization's current performance and the current and future needs and expectations of all interested parties?" There is not always a link between the analysis and specific objectives derived from such an analysis. Often an organization becomes inward-looking or desensitised to many issues in its environment as it cannot deal with all of them and not all are important. But the background changes and mechanisms should be in place to alert the organization of changes that will affect its performance. Testing relevance will require competent people who know what to look for and what to ignore.

Who is involved in this review?

If the organization is applying the **Involvement of people principle**, the audit should expect all levels to be involved in this review and information to be consolidated upwards through the organization. The auditor should also ask how outside agencies and sources have been used in these scanning activities. (Universities, technical institutions, research bodies, trade and professional associations). Objectives for individuals may no longer be relevant if the working environment has changed - if working from home has become more widespread or if technology has changed the way people work etc. Objectives for processes may no longer be relevant for the same reasons - if timescales have become compressed or cycle times reduced through more efficient ways of working. It is necessary to collect this information in order to balance the objectives in an organization.

How are the results of this review captured?

ISO 9001 clause 5.6.1 requires records from management reviews to be maintained and thus at the Enterprise level the auditor should expect to find records produced that describe the results of these reviews. At the Enterprise level, decisions are taken that may have a significant impact on the organization and therefore top management has to employ the **Factual approach principle** and be sure that the information upon which it makes its decisions is soundly based.

What methods are used to ensure the integrity of this information?

As information on the relevance of objectives passes up the hierarchy, there will be filtering as some of the facts meet resistance. The work environment in certain areas may act as a barrier to revealing this information. Hence it is important that the information that reaches the decision makers is confirmed fact, not opinion. Review meetings held at various levels in the organization may be the forum where the information is evaluated and decisions made, but the important factor is how the decisions are communicated.

How are the results conveyed to those responsible for taking action?

The focus is on the relevance of policies and objectives and therefore at the Enterprise level, changes in policies and objectives can have widespread impact. A change in a policy is more than a change to a document. The change is made with the intent that people change the way they do things and therefore the auditor needs to explore the communication strategy and determine whether the communication cycle has been repeated.

It is not unusual that during the communication process, some individuals and levels are missed. Employing the Involvement of people principle should guide the organizations to ensure that there is a process to ensure that all employees are involved. Importantly, this should also involve people when they join organizations outside the communication period.

What action was taken the last time these checks were performed that resulted in a change to the organization's policies and objectives?

The simplest way for an auditor to establish if the review process is working effectively is to trace the changes in policy and objectives back to the time the review was conducted. It is not necessary for every management review to result in changes to policies and objectives, but it depends upon the frequency of the review and how the organization ensures the integrity of the information.

Summary

This series of questions has focused on the Enterprise level - the **top management** - and as top management features very strongly in ISO 9001, it is pivotal to securing the evidence needed to verify that the organization has the capability to meet the requirements of the Standard. There can be conformity at other levels, but without a top management that exhibits commitment to process management; setting clear objectives, deploying them through use of the agreed policies (values), measuring achievement and striving for continual improvement, the system will not be effective. These are the tenets upon which ISO 9000 has been based and auditors must meet this challenge by asking these hard-hitting questions and not flinching from the goal. After gathering this evidence the auditor should be confident that the organization:

> *knows what it is trying to do*
>
> *knows how to make it happen*
>
> *knows that it's doing it right*
>
> *knows it is doing it in the best possible way*
>
> *knows that it is doing the right things*
>
> *is managing its performance.*

Chapter 6

Questions at the managerial level

ISO 9001 states that for an organization to function effectively, it has to identify and manage a set of interconnected processes. It is clear that the auditor should at this level; focus on a process and not on a function or a department or a procedure. When auditing at the Enterprise level, these processes will have been identified. Although the questions may be addressed to the Marketing Manager eg, it is the marketing process that is being examined not the marketing department or the marketing procedures. In the course of the interview, the manager may direct the auditor to other functions or departments for answers to their questions. As business processes comprise many sub-processes, the same methodology can be applied to these. At some level the business process resolves into work processes that individuals perform such as advertising, designing, making, packing or moving product and these are treated as the Operational level in the next Chapter.

Q1   What are you trying to do?

All processes are created to fulfil a purpose and therefore a key question is:

> *What is the purpose of the ******* process?*

(When using questions containing ***** these need to be replaced with the name of the process.)

Although the purpose of many processes may appear obvious, each organization may have created a process for a number of reasons apart from the obvious. For example the process established for maintaining physical resources may be of vital importance in the provision of air traffic control services but less significant in a business where external resources can be used in the event of failure.

The link between an organization's objectives and its processes is stated in ISO 9001 clause 5.4.2 where it requires the processes to meet the quality objectives. Clearly unless the purpose of the process is defined it is not possible to demonstrate that it is aligned with the specific objectives of the organization.

What is the ********* policy of the organization?

At the management level, the questions addressing "What are you trying to do?" are focused on **Policies and objectives**. The Business management process at the enterprise level generates the policies for the whole organization but there is a need to translate these into specific policies for each key business process as each has a different purpose and makes a different contribution to the organization's goals.

Goals
The aims of top management including its vision, values, mission, policies and objectives.

The particular policy for a process needs to guide those engaged in the process in the same direction as the organization's policies.

How does this policy relate to the organization's corporate policy?

There should be a match between local policy and corporate policy and the manager ought to be able to show how the local policies were derived. Any mismatch will indicate a potential for a process to produce results that do not meet the organization's corporate policies and objectives. This is a use of the **Leadership principle** in creating an appropriate work environment.

The organization's objectives will be expressed in terms that apply to the whole organization so these too may need to be translated into more specific objectives for each process.

What are the ******** objectives for the organization?

It should be possible for the management to demonstrate the linkage between the achievement of process objectives, the organization's purpose and its goals. Being shown a set of objectives does not indicate whether they are the right objectives. The auditor is not questioning the objectives themselves - it is the relationship between them that is important.

How do these objectives relate to the organizational goals and the ******** policy?

The objectives of a process should be derived from the objectives of the organization otherwise part of the organization will be driven in a different direction. Also the objectives for a process should be linked with the policies for that process otherwise the sets of values will not be appropriate or understood by those engaged in the process. As with the organizational policies and objectives it is important that the process objectives and policies are communicated.

> *How are the ****** policies and objectives communicated throughout the organization?*

ISO 9001 clause 5.5.3 addresses communication and it is fundamental to successful achievement that the policies and objectives are communicated. A significant cause of failure is a lack of understanding of requirements. It is therefore an important factor for the auditor to question.

> *How is understanding of these policies and objectives confirmed?*

As the policies and objectives are specific to a process, the auditor should expect measures for indicating the successful implementation of the policies and objectives to have been defined. In testing understanding, the auditor should expect management to use root cause analysis to discover clues as to why policies or objectives have not been understood.

Having established what the policies and objectives are for a particular process the auditor can move on to establishing how these objectives are achieved and these policies implemented.....

Q2   How do you make it happen?

No examination can start without the particular process being defined in clearly defined stages. Every organization is different and hence its processes will differ. The complexity, technology, product mix etc will all influence the particular sequence of activities needed to achieve the objectives.

> *What are the key stages in the process that have been established for achieving the ***** objectives?*

At the managerial level this question addresses the key stages in each business process. Each stage is a sub-process and will interact with the other sub-processes and with other business processes.

The auditee may respond with a detailed description of the process that covers more than just the key stages eg:

- The process objectives and process measures

- The key inputs and outputs

- The key stages and any appropriate procedures, instructions and information required to perform the activities

- The review and improvement mechanisms.

Having been given a picture of how the process is managed, the auditor is now able to probe the soundness and integrity of the inputs, outputs, methods and the results produced and therefore how these relate to the purpose of the organization and the requirements of the Standard.

In examining the response the auditor is seeking to establish that the sequence and interaction of these sub-processes is coherent and is related to the process objective(s). Each stage in a process produces an output that is an input to the next stage or to other processes. In order to control processes it is necessary to manage the outputs of each stage.

> *What specific outputs are required from each process stage?*

These outputs may be products, services or information in the form of decisions or documents. Every process should be designed to achieve specific objectives and the result will depend upon the extent to which the contributing factors have been anticipated and provisions made for compensating for their effects or preventing them from causing failure.

> ### *What analysis has been carried out to determine the factors that affect accomplishment of stage outputs?*

ISO 9001 clause 8.5.3 requires actions to prevent nonconformity to be determined and it is at the process design stage that such actions should be taken. A common method is to use a "What if?" analysis or Process Failure Modes and Effects Analysis (PFMEA). Other techniques are Design of Experiments, Critical Path Analysis, Data Flow Diagrams, Team Flow Diagrams, and Process Flow Diagrams etc. However, performing an analysis does not make things happen - the results of such analyses need to be used.

> ### *How have the results of this analysis been reflected in the design of the process?*

The auditor should be able to determine from the evidence provided that input and output criteria for each stage have been defined, that skills and competencies have been defined, that the source of information and resources are defined and link with other processes that provide them.

> ### *How do you know the process is capable of achieving the required objectives?*

Before a process is made operational it should be proved capable of delivering the required outputs, on time and within budget but this is not always feasible. ISO 9001 clause 8.2.3 requires processes to achieve planned results and therefore the organization should know how capable its processes are.

Clearly this is a preventive action aimed at reducing wastage of time, resources and cost as well as boosting confidence that the process outputs will meet the objectives. Process capability studies should therefore be carried out on all processes, not simply confined to those directly supplying product to customers.

Having established that the process has been design using soundly based methods, the auditor can move on to the measures used to demonstrate successful achievement of the required outputs.

> ## What specific measures are used to monitor successful achievement of these outputs?

Depending on the nature of the process, these measures could include units of production, achievement of milestones, reaching a level of maturity or capability, formulation of plans, specifications, recruitment of personnel, completed training. This question addresses ISO 9001 clause 4.1c, which requires criteria and methods to be determined to ensure the operation and control of these processes.

> ## What are the measurable targets for each of these key stages?

The targets are the quality, quantity and timing factors that need to be achieved. Those operating the process need to know these requirements to manage their work effectively. These requirements are the objectives for each stage and thus address clause 5.4.1 for quality objectives to be established at relevant functions and levels and also clause 7.1, which requires quality objectives and requirements for the product to be determined in planning product realization. In order to manage effectively, the performance of each of the key stages needs to be known.

> ## What methods of measurement are used and how often are measurements taken?

The methods of measurement will vary depending on what is being measured. In the design process it may be design review, in the production process it may be inspection and test, in the purchasing process it may be supplier evaluation, and in personnel development it may be appraisal or competence assessment. Evidence should be sought by the auditor to demonstrate that the methods and frequency of measurement are soundly based and appropriate. This is applying the **Factual approach principle**.

> ## How is the integrity of the method of measurement maintained to ensure consistency of measurement?

All measurement whether physical or not should be accurate and hence where the measuring device is human, the person must be competent (a requirement of ISO 9001 clause 6.2.1). In physical terms this may relate to measuring devices that will require calibration against appropriate standards of known accuracy and precision. In this context, ISO 9001 clause 7.6 applies. Where the measuring device is a review or an evaluation, integrity is often assured by use of experts or specialist personnel and independent review.

The measurements generate data, some of which may be transient, but in order to manage the process and take subsequent action, information needs to be recorded.

> ## How are the results of measurement captured?

The response to this question addresses ISO 9001 clause 4.2.4, which requires records to be established and maintained to provide evidence of conformity. The auditor should establish that the data recorded relates to the measurable outputs defined for the process and the key stages. Those on the scene of the action may take the measurements but may not be authorised to take action.

> ## How are the results of measurements conveyed to those responsible for taking action?

In many cases action is not taken on every measurement. Trends are plotted and analysis performed to convert measurements into meaningful information. This is an opportunity to establish the soundness of the information flow by asking why data is to be collected and where it is used.

> ## What action was taken the last time these checks were performed that resulted in improved stage output?

The response to this question will establish whether the organization is undertaking corrective action as required by ISO 9001 clause 8.5.2 or is simply concerned with correcting errors thus responding to ISO 9001 clause 8.3 on the control of nonconforming product.

Once the plans have been devised, there are four key factors that affect success as defined by the measurable outputs. The first is the competence of personnel; the second is the capability of the physical resource, the third, is the work environment and the fourth the information used to carry out the work. The examination of the human and physical resource management processes will reveal whether the process inputs (people, equipment, components, buildings, facilities and finance) are likely to be correct. If these resourcing processes have been proven effective, there is no reason to re-examine them in every process apart from random integrity or cross checks. The physical work environment is established when setting up a process and will be addressed by the process development process. The human work environment is established through the organization's policies and values and the examination of the business management process will reveal whether these conditions are likely to be in place. Again there is no reason to re-examine this apart from random integrity checks, which can be easily established by assessment of people's responses to the questions and the issues that have been raised.

> ## What information is necessary for each stage in the *******
> ## process to be performed as planned?

Within each process, information and its flow through the process is an integral part of the process and both are determined by the outputs required at each stage. ISO 9001 clause 4.1d) requires the information necessary to support the operation and control of processes to be available. Information needed by the process may be in many forms. Plans, specifications, reports, records, contracts, orders, instructions, procedures etc., but it also needs to be communicated. There will be many ways in which personnel acquire the information they need to execute a process stage. An important method of communication will be the training/induction of the people involved in the process. The auditor needs to establish that organizations have selected the most appropriate method to transmit the information.

> ## How is this information communicated to the staff who perform
> ## the planned activities?

The information could be transmitted verbally, discovered by observation or acquired through training, culture or habit. It does not have to be in the form of procedures or documents. ISO 9001 clause 4.2.1c) requires documents needed by the organization to ensure the effective planning, operation and control of its processes to be determined. It also requires in clause 4.2.3 that documents be controlled.

> ## How is the currency, validity and integrity of this information maintained?

The integrity of information is vital to process capability and although the organization may have in place a document control process, it does not follow that all information required to operate a process will necessarily be governed by this process. The scope of document control will be defined within and between each process to ensure effective communication. The auditor therefore needs to establish the scope of the information control system and establish how the information identified as a result of the previous question all falls within the scope of this process. In asking about the currency of information the auditor is addressing ISO 9001 clause 4.2.3d), validity is addressed by clause 4.2.3a) and integrity by clauses 4.2.3b), c), e), f) and g).

With some processes not producing measurable results until long after the outputs have been delivered, there is a need for confidence that the activities are being carried out as intended. Managers may walk the floor, periodically check progress and hold meetings to keep abreast of what is going on.

> ## How do you know that the ***** activities are being performed as planned?

Although a lot of effort may be put into ensuring the planning is right, at best, plans are estimates of what is necessary. It is often unwise to rely on predictions and foresight alone as there may well be factors that have been overlooked when attempting to anticipate events that could jeopardise success.

The auditor needs to establish that there is a soundly based method used by management to monitor that activities are being performed as planned and that these activities are in fact being performed. One method is self-audit, another is independent audit either internal (as required by clause 8.2.2) or external.

All processes should possess provision for dealing with situations when things do not proceed as planned.

> ## What action is carried out when activities are not performed as planned?

These actions may be identified in various forms, including escalation procedures, troubleshooting and diagnostic methods and problem-solving. The auditor should evaluate the response for evidence that the provisions built into the process for such situations are being followed.

Having established how the process objectives are to be achieved the auditor can move on to explore the process by which the organization determines the extent to which the process objectives are actually being achieved.....

Q3   How do you know it's right?

Here the auditor is examining the process in action - how the process is performing against the process objectives.

> *What measures are used to verify achievement of the*
> ******* *objectives and what target values have been agreed?*

At the Managerial level, these measures relate to process outputs and therefore will be a sub-set of the organization's corporate objectives. In some cases the organization's objective may be achieved through one process but more often several processes form a chain to deliver the required results and each has distinct objectives. The auditor is verifying that the measures actually being used are those planned.

> *How are the results of measuring process output captured?*

The auditor should seek out the actual results to demonstrate that the planned results of measurements are available for subsequent action.

For design reviews there should be records of the results of the review as required by ISO 9001 clause 7.3.4 and for products, there should be records containing the results of measurements, the acceptance criteria and the identity of the person judging acceptability as required by ISO 9001 clause 8.2.4.

> *What results are being achieved against these targets?*

This question may be asked at any stage, but it is important that there is a link between the achieved results and the planned objectives. In examining the results the auditor is not concerned with the figures themselves but with the relationship between objectives, targets, measures and results. Where results are below target, the auditor can ask what is being done to identify the cause and bring performance upto target. Often results show progress towards an objective, therefore no action may be necessary but the trend may indicate slow progress that could be questioned.

What methods of measurement are used and how often are measurements taken?

The method of measuring process outputs will vary depending on the nature of the output. In many cases it may be a document review, a design review or product verification. For document reviews the auditor should examine evidence to establish that documents are reviewed when changes are made as ISO 9001 clause 4.2.3b) requires documents to be reviewed and updated. For design reviews the auditor should probe to establish that reviews are held at appropriate stages as required by ISO 9001 clause 7.3.4. For product verification the auditor should probe to establish that incoming product is verified as required by ISO 9001 clause 7.4.3 and that outgoing product is verified as required by ISO 9001 clause 8.2.4.

Whether the measurements are of documents, designs or products, the integrity of measurement is important in producing valid results.

What methods are used to ensure the integrity of these measurements?

The integrity of the results of document reviews is dependent upon the competency and independence of the reviewers and the criteria employed and therefore the auditor should establish that these factors are defined and sound methods used for document reviews. In a similar way, the integrity of design reviews is dependent upon having competent personnel to review the design. The auditor should look for actual evidence of 'calibration activity' eg instruments, training in agreed or standard methods/methodologies, agreed interviewing techniques.

How are the results conveyed to those responsible for taking action?

In product realization processes, the same person that takes the action may collect the results but in other cases additional competencies may be required to analyse the problems and devise a plan of action. There may be therefore various routes that such information may take in a process and the organization needs to have provided for those that have been anticipated.

> *What analysis has been performed to determine the cause in the difference between actual and planned results?*

ISO 9001 clause 8.4 requires data to be analysed as does clauses 8.5.2 and 8.5.3 on corrective and preventive action. The auditor should look for evidence that the root cause of the difference has been established when examining the evidence. The detail of the records is not crucial to the auditor but evidence of action taken as a result is important in demonstrating that the organization has its processes under control. The actions taken as a result of measurement will be either to proceed to the next process or to perform some remedial action in order to correct deficiencies.

> *What action was taken the last time these checks were performed that resulted in a better overall performance?*

All actions taken should result in improvement as required by ISO 9001 clauses 8.4 and 8.5.1. Improvement can be demonstrated quite simply from records of measurements showing that the actions taken had a beneficial effect. It comes down to what the objectives are and what measures and targets are used to indicate achievement. If the objective is for improved delivery performance and the measure is % on-time delivery, the auditor should look for improvement in the results and examine the actions that caused the change in performance. If the organization can demonstrate that certain planned actions caused the change, improvement has been demonstrated. If no relationship between the result and any planned actions can be demonstrated, the organization has not yet got its processes under control.

Even when an organization achieves its objectives, they cannot afford to rest on their laurels as competition forces them to look for more efficient ways of producing the same result to drive down costs and shorten delivery or response times. At the managerial level this means finding better processes. Not only is the quest for improving the processes a requirement of ISO 9001 clause 8.1, but knowledge and technology change so rapidly that management also needs to frequently question its practices and this is the next area for the auditor to explore.....

Q4   How do you know it's the best way of doing it?

Continual improvement is about finding better ways of doing things but if the organization is to make continual improvement, a systematic approach to improvement needs to be in place. Relying on the random identification of improvements is not a recurring activity to increase the ability to fulfil requirements and hence is not continuous. As stated previously, a process is a set of interrelated tasks, behaviours and resources that achieve a result. Behaviours are conditioned by the policies and as the policies are likely to have been developed on the basis that their implementation would produce consistent results, if the policies are implemented as intended, consistent results should be achieved.

> *What checks are used to verify that the manner in which the ***** process is implemented is consistent with the organization's policies and values?*

The checks performed to determine whether the way actions and decisions are taken are consistent with the policy may not be separate checks. It may be more appropriate to ask this question when examining the policies themselves. Another way of asking this question is for the auditor to ask whether policy implementation is confirmed at key decision points in the process, following which evidence that such criteria is being applied can be looked for.

As stated previously, continual improvement is about finding better ways of doing things and therefore the organization should have in place stages in the process that continually question whether the way things are done could be improved.

> *What checks are used to verify the activities carried out are best practice?*

The auditor should establish whether the organization reviews the process to find better ways of achieving the same result eg Is there a better process that could be used to produce the same outputs? Has the organization benchmarked this process against similar processes in the same organization, sister companies or the same industry sector?

> ## How is best practice defined?

At the process level, there should be many opportunities to benchmark processes and process stages against other parts of the organization and other organizations. There may also be standards, industry practices and guidelines that help define best practice. The criteria does not need to be definitive in great detail. A simple model, diagram, flow chart, case study or description can define best practice.

> ## What methods are used to conduct these checks and how often are they performed?

In many organizations there is a fear or loathing of what other organizations do. A "Not Invented Here Syndrome" may prevail such that the organization becomes very arrogant about its practices. The auditor should not be put off by such reactions and ask about productivity assessments in order to establish that there is evidence that operations are being run efficiently. At the process level, those involved in the process should participate in searching for best practice and their contributions should be welcomed. Such an approach is proof of the application of the Involvement in people principle.

> ## Who is involved in this assessment?

An organization that pursues best practice would involve all its people in one form or another. There may be departmental and multifunctional improvement teams working on improvement projects. In addition to internal staff being involved, others outside the process should also be involved, eg the receivers of the process outputs and the suppliers of the process inputs. In this way the organization is applying the 1st and the 8th principle of quality management.

The results of the assessment should be recorded but as the checks may be conducted over different timescales and in different locations there is a need to collect this data for analysis as required by ISO 9001 clause 8.4.

> ## How are the results of this assessment captured?

The results from assessments of best practice are likely to be in the form of reports containing an analysis of benchmarking, surveys, literature searches, technical papers and other information. The key findings and conclusions should be identified together with action plans and targets that aim to improve current practice.

> *How are these results conveyed to those responsible for taking action?*

Process improvement needs to be co-ordinated and the auditor should therefore expect the process owners to be actively involved in managing the improvement effort. Projects that pursue improvements in practice are often abandoned as other projects are given higher priority. The initiators may therefore be unaware of progress or the reasons for delay.

> *What improvement in results was obtained from the last review of the ***** process?*

The auditor should question several people in the process to establish that the actions resulting from improvement projects are plainly obvious to those at the sharp end. If they cannot see any difference, or are unaware of any changes it is likely that the practices have not changed. This aspect is addressed in ISO 9001 clause 5.5.3, which requires top management to ensure that communication takes place regarding the effectiveness of the system.

> *How was this improvement measured?*

As with any improvement, performance needs to be measured before and after the change. In this case the change in performance might be exhibited by an improvement in productivity, response time, cycle time or reduction in rework. The auditor should seek the data that demonstrates improvement has occurred. The figures themselves are of no concern to the auditor - it is whether any beneficial change took place.

The process may deliver the required result in the best way but management needs to question whether these results are still required. This is the next area for the auditor to explore.....

Q5   How do you know it's the right thing to do?

At the process level, it is easy to lose sight of the objectives when all effort is focused on processing information or product and delivering results to the next process or to customers and suppliers. Objectives are often changed to reflect current priorities or become subservient to current pressures. It is therefore necessary for the auditor to establish that the process owner still has his/her eye on the ball! In other words, that the process is delivering the right results to the right location at the right time.

> *What checks are carried out to verify the ***** objectives remain relevant to the achievement of the organization's corporate policy and objectives?*

The management review in ISO 9001 is often interpreted as a single meeting but in order for top management to make decisions based on fact (the **Factual approach principle**) information has to be channelled from the coalface to the boardroom. Therefore process reviews should take place where the same questions that apply at the Enterprise level are asked at each level. The context is all that is different. The auditor would therefore expect to find periodic process reviews taking place. Some of the corporate objectives may well have been established from a consolidation of objectives that were gathered from individual processes and therefore a review of these objectives is wholly consistent with this approach.

> *What methods are used to conduct these checks and how often are they performed?*

At the managerial level, the focus will be on satisfying particular customers, orders, targets etc and these will influence the validity of the process objectives. Being closer to the customer at the managerial level, the process owners become more aware of whether they are going in the right direction and are able to change course more quickly. In changing course they may divert resources away from achieving the organization's objectives and therefore the methods used to perform these checks and the frequency of the checks need to be balanced with the rate of change in the process. Some processes remain stable for long periods whereas others are constantly changing to keep pace with the external environment.

> ## Who is involved in this review?

Changes in the environment that affect all people should be dealt with at the Enterprise level. However, some changes affect only one or two groups of people such as in the Service Delivery Process. Those at the customer interface may bring more insight into what needs to change than those who are remote. At the managerial level therefore the review of objectives can become more focused and deal with issues that only apply to those operating the process. The auditor therefore needs to establish that the appropriate people are involved and that their contribution is welcomed. Any examination of objectives should involve those they affect if the organization is applying the Involvement of people principle. The results of this review should be recorded so that they can be communicated and as stated previously, they need to be communicated upwards so that consolidation of results occurs. They also need to be communicated for action.

> ## How are the results of this review captured?

Decisions to change process policies and objectives or in fact leave them unchanged, are not decisions to be taken lightly. Such decisions need facts and the organization should therefore be applying the Factual approach principle.

> ## What methods are used to ensure the integrity of this information?

The process owners should be aware that as facts pass up through the organization some filtering would take place. This is often caused by the reviewers not being presented with irrefutable evidence that the policies and objectives are sound or really do need to be changed. The auditor should therefore look for evidence that the process teams have taken sufficient action to give confidence in the results and presented their conclusions in a way that will attract the attention of top management. In some cases the responsibility for action resulting from these assessments remains within the process. In other cases the responsibility lies outside the process - perhaps with top management.

> ## How are the results conveyed to those responsible for taking action?

The focus is on the relevance of policies and objectives and therefore at the Managerial level, changes in policies and objectives will impact those who contribute to the process under review. Any change in a process needs to be examined in the light of its effects on the organization as a whole. However, all changes in policy and objectives should result in people doing things differently. The auditor needs to explore the communication strategy and determine whether the communication cycle has been repeated.

> ## What action was taken the last time these checks were performed that resulted in a change to the ****** policies and objectives?

The simplest way for an auditor to establish if the review process is working effectively is to trace the changes in policy and objectives back to the time the review was conducted. It is not necessary for every process review to result in changes to policies and objectives, but it depends upon the frequency of the review and how the organization ensures the integrity of the information.

Summary

This series of questions has focused on the Managerial level - the level that manages processes. ISO 9001 clause 4.1 requires that processes are managed and these series of questions have focused on the factors that affect the ability of management to manage processes effectively. Effectively managed processes are those in which there is strong leadership, the involvement of people and suppliers, management by fact and a strong framework for setting objectives, deploying them, measuring achievement and striving for continual improvement. Documentation has not featured prominently in these questions because it is a vehicle to communicate information and no more. Questions about documentation are secondary and therefore have not been included in any detail. The process will not be effective unless targets are set, performance measured and actions taken to improve performance. Audits of processes should therefore focus on results and establish whether the methods to achieve these results are soundly based. These are the tenets upon which ISO 9000 has been based and auditors must meet this challenge by asking these hard-hitting questions and not flinching from the goal. After gathering this evidence the auditor should be confident that management:

knows what the process aims to achieve

knows how to design and cause processes to achieve results

knows that it's doing it right

knows that it is doing it in the best possible way

knows that it is doing the right things

is regulating performance.

Chapter 7

Questions at the operational level

At the operational level, the auditor is examining work processes that are either operated by individuals or groups of individuals. Before approaching an individual, auditors should have identified the area of the process to be explored and therefore commence the interview with knowledge of what they are trying to establish and with the expectation that the person is the right person to provide the information required.

The questions asked would be similar to those previously asked but focused on specific operations. As the rationale behind the questions is the same as before, they are provided simply as a list.

Q1   What are you trying to do?

- What role do you play in the ******** process?
- What is the purpose of these activities?
- What are your objectives relative to these activities?

Q2   How do you make it happen?

- What criteria need to be satisfied before work can commence?
- What information and resources are needed to carry out this work?
- What action is taken to prepare the inputs for processing?
- What are the key steps in this process?
- What do you do when things don't go as planned?

Q3   How do you know it's right?

- What measures are used to verify achievement of your objectives?
- What target values have been agreed?
- What results are you achieving against these targets?

- What methods of measurement are used and how often are measurements taken?

- How do you ensure the integrity of these measurements?

- How are the results of measuring process output captured?

- What analysis is performed to determine the cause in the difference between actual and planned results?

- What improvement in results was obtained from the last review of these activities?

Q4 How do you know you are doing it in the best possible way?

- How do you know that you are ***** in the best way?

- What checks have been performed to verify that the methods used are best practice?

- How is best practice defined?

Q5 How do you know you are doing the right things?

- When did you last confirm that your objectives were relevant to achieving the organization's objectives?

- Who is involved in this review?

- What action was taken from the last review that resulted in a change to your objectives?

Summary

This series of questions has focused on the Operational level - the level at which process stages and tasks are performed. After gathering this evidence the auditor should be confident that individuals:

> *know what they are supposed to do*
>
> *know that they are doing it right*
>
> *know that they are doing it in the best way*
>
> *know that they are doing the right things*
>
> *are regulating their own performance.*

Chapter 8

Assessing business processes

The questioning strategy addressed in Chapters 5, 6 & 7 was based upon three hierarchical levels that are present in many organizations. In terms of the business processes that may exist in an organization, the Business Management Process applies to the Enterprise level and all other business processes apply to the Managerial level. In terms of people, the top management may include managers of business processes, but when they are interviewed within the Business Management Process, they are executives sharing responsibility for the enterprise. When they are being interviewed within other business processes they are either the process owner or a manager having responsibility for a major stage within a process. At some stage they may also act at the operational level, performing tasks like everyone else in the organization. It is not unusual to find managers spending a percentage of their time on executive issues, a percentage on managerial issues and a percentage on operational issues. When assessing a business process it is therefore likely that the auditor will travel the breadth and depth of the organization, often returning to a person to carry out an interview on a different topic than before at a different level in the hierarchy. When a heating engineer checks a heating system, the checks are not confined to one room. The heating engineer will go through every room testing a part of the system that is located in each room, but will spend most of the time in the boiler room where the power is generated!

In this Chapter, the questioning methodology explained in Chapter 4 is applied to several business processes. These may not be the actual processes found in an organization. The auditor will need to identify the business processes that exist in each organization being audited. In each sample process there are generic questions that apply to all processes and those that are specific to a particular process. Although there is considerable repetition, it should be noted that the questions are asked of different people in a different context each time and therefore will elicit different responses. The lists are not intended to be comprehensive but the questions should trigger a line of enquiry that tracks through all the processes in an organization and examines activities where conformity with the requirements of ISO 9001 can be demonstrated.

Business management process

Process description

For the purpose of this book the business management process creates the vision, the mission and the overall strategy for the organization. Taking market research data from the marketing process, external standards, laws and other constraints, this strategy delivers the policies and objectives for the organization to fulfil in order to create and retain satisfied customers. The business management process also monitors performance and manages both strategic and tactical changes to deliver the desired results for all stakeholders.

Business policies

The purpose of examining the business policies is to establish that the organization is focused on satisfying customers and other interested parties in accomplishing its purpose/mission.

1. What is the purpose/mission of the organization?

2. What analysis has been carried out to determine the critical factors that affect accomplishment of the purpose/mission?

3. How were these factors identified and evaluated?

4. What policies have been established to guide the organization in accomplishing its purpose/mission?

5. What is the process by which policies are established?

6. How are the organization's policies communicated throughout the organization?

7. How have those responsible for implementing these policies been involved in their development?

8. What measures are used to indicate successful implementation of these policies?

9. How is understanding of these policies confirmed?

Business planning

The purpose of examining business planning is to establish that the organization's methods for achieving its mission and implementing its policies are soundly based.

1. What are the key stages in the process used to establish the objectives and processes for achieving the organization's goals?

2. What analysis has been carried out to understand the current and future needs and expectations of all interested parties?

3. What analysis has been carried out to determine the organization's current performance and capability?

4. What research was carried out to validate these factors?

5. How do you maintain the integrity of the results of these analyses?

6. How do you determine the relevant statutory and regulatory requirements that impact the mission?

7. What objectives have been established as a result of this research to enable the organization to achieve its purpose/mission?

8. What analysis has been carried out to balance these objectives and set priorities for action?

9. What products, services, markets, projects are necessary to achieve these objectives?

10. Which products, services, markets, projects need to be abandoned, as they do not fulfil these objectives?

11. How are the risks to achieving these objectives identified and evaluated?

12. What set of interconnected processes have been established to deliver the required products and services to customers?

13. What processes are required to withdraw obsolete products and services and abandon projects that are no longer required?

14. What analysis is carried out to determine the organizational structure and work environment needed to deliver these processes?

15. What is the organization structure that results from this analysis?

16. How have those responsible for operating these processes been involved in their development?

17. How are the plans for achieving the organization's objectives deployed within the organization?

18. How do you ensure the plans for achieving the organization's objectives are understood?

19. How is the currency, validity and integrity of the information contained in these plans maintained?

Business review and improvement

Achievement of business objectives

The purpose of examining the achievement of business objectives is to establish that the organization is using soundly based methods for their measurement. The specific targets and performance levels are of no concern to the auditor. Trends may provide evidence of continual improvement.

1. What measures are used to verify achievement of the organization's objectives and what target values have been agreed?

2. What results are being achieved against these targets?

3. What specific measures are used to verify that the organization is satisfying the needs and expectations of all interested parties?

4. What methods of measurement are used and how often are measurements taken?

5. What methods are used to ensure the integrity of these measurements?

6. How are the results of measuring business performance captured?

7. How are the results conveyed to those responsible for taking action?

8. What analysis has been performed to determine the cause of the difference between actual and planned results?

9. What improvement in results was obtained from the last review of the organization's overall performance?

Business system effectiveness

The purpose in examining the effectiveness of the management system is to establish that the best ways of achieving the organization's objectives are being used.

1. What checks are used to verify that the manner in which the system is implemented is consistent with the organization's policies and values?

2. What results were obtained the last time these checks were performed?

3. What checks are used to verify that the system for achieving the organization's policies and objectives is effective?

4. What results were obtained the last time these checks were performed?

5. What are the criteria for determining whether the system is effective?

6. What methods are used to conduct these checks and how often are they performed?

7. Who is involved in this assessment?

8. How are the results of this assessment captured?

9. How are these results conveyed to those responsible for taking action?

10. What improvement in results was obtained from the last review of system effectiveness?

11. How was this improvement measured?

Relevance of business policies and objectives

The purpose in examining the relevance of the organization's policy and objectives is to establish that soundly based methods are in place to improve alignment of these goals with the organization's purpose/mission.

1. What checks are carried out to verify that the organization's objectives remain relevant to the achievement of its purpose/mission?

2. What methods are used to conduct these checks and how often are they performed?

3. Who is involved in this review?

4. How are the results of this review captured?

5. What methods are used to ensure the integrity of this information?

6. How are the results conveyed to those responsible for taking action?

7. What action was taken the last time these checks were performed that resulted in a change to the organization's policies and objectives?

Marketing process

Process description

For the purpose of this book the marketing process seeks out customer's current unfulfilled needs and expectations, translates these into the organization's capability and delivers potential customers into the sales process. The process predicts customer future needs that are vital to the business management process in forming the organization's strategy. The marketing process also delivers new opportunities into the product development process so that new products and services may be created to satisfy customer needs and expectations. In some organizations, marketing includes sales and distribution and in some organizations may include product development. In this book these are classed as separate business processes and in some cases may be outsourced.

Marketing policies and objectives

The purpose in examining marketing policies and objectives is to establish that the marketing effort is focused on customer satisfaction and consistent with the organization's corporate policies and objectives.

1. What is the purpose of the marketing process?
2. What is the marketing policy of the organization?
3. How does this policy relate to the organization's corporate policy?
4. What are the marketing objectives for the organization?
5. What is the process by which these objectives are established?
6. How do these objectives relate to the organizational goals and the marketing policy?
7. How are the marketing policies and objectives communicated throughout the organization?
8. How is understanding of these policies and objectives confirmed?

Marketing activities

The purpose in examining marketing activities is to establish that the organization's methods for identifying, determining, translating and communicating customer needs and expectations are soundly based.

Generic

1. What are the key stages in the process that have been established for achieving the marketing objectives?

2. What specific outputs are required from each stage in the marketing process?

3. What analysis has been carried out to determine the factors that affect accomplishment of stage outputs?

4. How have the results of this analysis been reflected in the design of the marketing process?

5. How do you know the process is capable of achieving the required marketing objectives?

6. What specific measures are used to monitor successful achievement of these outputs?

7. What are the measurable targets for each of these key stages?

8. What methods of measurement are used and how often are measurements taken?

9. How is the integrity of the method of measurement maintained to ensure consistency of measurement?

10. How are the results of measurement captured?

11. How are the results of measurement conveyed to those responsible for taking action?

12. What action was taken the last time these checks were performed that resulted in improved stage output?

13. What information in the marketing process is necessary for each stage to be performed as planned?

14. How is this information communicated to the staff who perform the planned marketing activities?

15. How is the currency, validity and integrity of this information maintained?

16. How do you know that the marketing activities are being performed as planned?

17. What action is carried out when marketing activities are not performed as planned?

Specific

1. What analysis has been carried out to understand the market segments in which the organization operates?

2. What analysis has been carried out to identify the factors necessary for the organization to succeed in creating customers in its chosen market segments?

3. What research was carried out to validate these factors?

4. How did you determine the resources necessary to carry out this research?

5. How do you maintain the integrity of the results of this research?

6. How do you identify the current and future needs and expectations of all customers in the chosen market segments?

7. What factors were identified to determine customer perceptions of the quality of the organization's products and services?

8. How did you establish which of the customer needs and expectations the organization should concentrate on?

9. How were these needs and expectations translated into requirements for product or service design, production or service delivery and distribution?

10. How are these marketing requirements communicated within the organization?

11. How do you ensure the marketing requirements are understood?

12. How do you maintain the currency, validity and integrity of the marketing requirements?

Marketing review and improvement

Achievement of marketing objectives

The purpose in examining the achievement of marketing objectives is to establish that:

a) the organization is using soundly based methods for their accomplishment

b) the organizational objectives are being achieved

c) the organization is producing the products and services that satisfy customer needs and expectations.

1. What measures are used to verify achievement of the marketing objectives and what target values have been agreed?

2. What specific measures are used to verify that the organization's products and services meet customer needs and expectations?

3. How are the results of measuring customer satisfaction captured?

4. What results are being achieved?

5. What methods of measurement are used and how often are measurements taken?

6. What methods are used to ensure the integrity of these measurements?

7. How are the results conveyed to those responsible for taking action?

8. What analysis has been performed to determine the cause of the difference between actual and planned results?

9. What improvement in results was obtained from the last review of the marketing process?

Marketing process effectiveness

The purpose in examining the effectiveness of the marketing process is to establish that the best ways of achieving the marketing objectives are being used.

1. What checks are used to verify that the manner in which the marketing process is implemented is consistent with the organization's policies and values?

2. What checks are used to verify the activities being carried out are best practice?

3. How is best practice defined?

4. What methods are used to conduct these checks and how often are they performed?

5. Who is involved in this assessment?

6. How are the results of this assessment captured?

7. How are these results conveyed to those responsible for taking action?

8. What improvement in effectiveness was obtained when the marketing process was last reviewed?

9. How was this improvement measured?

Relevance of policies and objectives

The purpose in examining the relevance of marketing policy and objectives is to establish that the organization has soundly based methods in place to improve alignment of these goals with the corporate policy.

1. What checks are carried out to verify that the marketing objectives remain relevant to the achievement of the organization's corporate policy and objectives?

2. What methods are used to conduct these checks and how often are they performed?

3. Who is involved in this review?

4. How are the results of this review captured?

5. What methods are used to ensure the integrity of this information?

6. How are the results conveyed to those responsible for taking action?

7. What action was taken the last time these checks were performed that resulted in a change to the marketing policies and objectives?

Sales process

Process description

For the purpose of this book the sales process promotes the organization and its products and services, makes contact with customers for existing products and services, handles customer enquiries and processes contracts/orders. As a consequence of these actions, the sales process delivers requirements into product development, production and service delivery processes or directly into the distribution process if product/service is already available for supply.

Sales policies and objectives

The purpose in examining sales goals is to establish that the sales effort is focused on customer satisfaction and consistent with the organization's corporate policies and objectives.

1. What is the purpose of the sales process?
2. What is the sales policy of the organization?
3. How does this policy relate to the organization's corporate policy?
4. What are the sales objectives for the organization?
5. What is the process by which these objectives are established?
6. How do these objectives relate to the organizational goals and the sales policy?
7. How are the sales policies and objectives communicated throughout the organization?
8. How is understanding of these policies and objectives confirmed?

Sales activities

The purpose in examining sales activities is to establish that the methods for selling the organization and its products and services are soundly based.

Generic
1. What are the key stages in the process that have been established for achieving the sales objectives?
2. What specific outputs are required for each stage in the sales process?

3. What analysis has been carried out to determine the factors that affect accomplishment of stage outputs?

4. How have the results of this analysis been reflected in the design of the sales process?

5. How do you know the process is capable of achieving the required sales objectives?

6. What specific measures are used to monitor successful achievement of these outputs?

7. What are the measurable targets for each of these key stages?

8. What methods of measurement are used and how often are measurements taken?

9. How is the integrity of the method of measurement maintained to ensure consistency of measurement?

10. How are the results of measurement captured?

11. How are the results of measurement conveyed to those responsible for taking action?

12. What action was taken the last time these checks were performed that resulted in improved stage output?

13. What information in the sales process is necessary for each stage to be performed as planned?

14. How is this information communicated to the staff who perform the planned sales activities?

15. How is the currency, validity and integrity of this information maintained?

16. How do you know that the sales activities are being performed as planned?

17. What action is carried out when sales activities are not performed as planned?

Specific

1. What analysis has been carried out to understand the environment into which the organization intends to offer its products and services?

2. What analysis has been carried out to identify the factors necessary for the organization to succeed in attracting and retaining customers in its chosen market segment?

3. What promotional and pricing strategy has been developed to achieve the sales objectives as a result of this analysis?

4. What are the principal activities of the process by which the organization promotes its products and services and in what order are they performed?

5. How is information on the organization's products and services conveyed to potential customers and how is its integrity maintained?

6. What are the principal activities of the process by which customer enquiries are converted into sales and in what order are they performed?

7. What inputs trigger order processes and from where do they originate?

8. How do you determine whether the products and services the organization offers will satisfy the needs of potential customers?

9. How do you determine whether the organization has the capability to satisfy customer requirements before accepting orders?

10. How are risks to meeting customer requirements identified and managed?

11. How are customer requirements captured, accepted and conveyed to those responsible for their implementation?

12. How have those providing the product or service been involved in accepting customer requirements?

13. How do you ensure the requirements of the order/contract are understood?

14. How do you maintain the currency, validity and integrity of the order/contract requirements?

15. What is the process by which changes to orders/contracts are managed?

16. How are changes in orders/contracts captured, accepted and conveyed to those responsible for their implementation?

Sales review and improvement

Achievement of sales objectives

The purpose in examining the achievement of sales objectives is to establish that:

a) the organization is using soundly based methods for their accomplishment

b) the organizational objectives are being achieved

c) the organization is supplying products and services that satisfy customer needs and expectations.

1. What measures are used to verify achievement of the sales objectives and what target values have been agreed?

2. What checks are carried out to verify that the customers receive the products and service they have ordered?

3. What methods of measurement are used and how often are measurements taken?

4. What methods are used to ensure the integrity of these measurements?

5. How are the results of measurement captured?

6. How are the results conveyed to those responsible for taking action?

7. What analysis has been performed to determine the cause in the difference between actual and planned results?

8. What improvement in results was obtained from the last review of the sales process?

Sales process effectiveness

The purpose in examining the effectiveness of the sales process is to establish that the best ways of achieving the objectives are being used.

1. What checks are used to verify that the manner in which the sales process is implemented is consistent with the organization's policies and values?

2. What checks are used to verify the activities being carried out are best practice?

3. How is best practice defined?

4. What methods are used to conduct these checks and how often are they performed?

5. Who is involved in this assessment?

6. How are the results of this assessment captured?

7. How are these results conveyed to those responsible for taking action?

8. What improvement in effectiveness was obtained when the sales process was last reviewed?

9. How was this improvement measured?

Relevance of sales policies and objectives

The purpose in examining the relevance of sales policy and objectives is to establish that the organization has in place soundly based methods to improve alignment of these goals with the corporate policy.

1. What checks are carried out to verify that the sales objectives remain relevant to the achievement of the organization's corporate policy and objectives?

2. What methods are used to conduct these checks and how often are they performed?

3. Who is involved in this review?

4. How are the results of this review captured?

5. What methods are used to ensure the integrity of this information?

6. How are the results conveyed to those responsible for taking action?

7. What action was taken the last time these checks were performed that resulted in a change to the sales policies and objectives?

Finance management process

Process description

Triggered by the organization's objectives and requirements of specific customers, projects and initiatives, the financial management process identifies, acquires, maintains and manages the financial resources needed to fulfil its objectives.

Finance policies and objectives

The purpose in examining finance policies and objectives is to establish that the financial resources and management support the achievement of customer satisfaction and are consistent with the organization's corporate policies and objectives.

1. What is the purpose of the finance process?
2. What is the finance policy of the organization?
3. How does this policy relate to the organization's corporate policy?
4. What are the finance objectives for the organization?
5. What is the process by which these objectives are established?
6. How do these objectives relate to the organizational goals and the finance policy?
7. How are the finance policies and objectives communicated throughout the organization?
8. How is understanding of these policies and objectives confirmed?

Finance activities

The purpose in examining finance activities is to establish that the organization's methods for controlling financial resources are compatible with the organization's other objectives.

Generic
1. What are the key stages in the process that have been established for achieving the financial objectives?
2. What specific outputs are for each stage in the financial process?

3. What analysis has been carried out to determine the factors that affect accomplishment of stage outputs?

4. How have the results of this analysis been reflected in the design of the financial process?

5. How do you know the process is capable of achieving the required financial objectives?

6. What are the specific measures used to monitor successful achievement of these outputs?

7. What are the measurable targets for each of these key stages?

8. What methods of measurement are used and how often are measurements taken?

9. How is the integrity of the method of measurement maintained to ensure consistency of measurement?

10. How are the results of measurement captured?

11. How are the results of measurement conveyed to those responsible for taking action?

12. What action was taken the last time these checks were performed that resulted in improved stage output?

13. What information in the financial process is necessary for each stage to be performed as planned?

14. How is this information communicated to the staff who perform the planned financial activities?

15. How is the currency, validity and integrity of this information maintained?

16. How do you know that the financial activities are being performed as planned?

17. What action is carried out when financial activities are not performed as planned?

Specific
1. How are the personnel in the finance management process made aware of their contribution to achieving customer satisfaction?

2. How are customer satisfaction and product quality criteria determined for use in investment decisions?

3. How is the value and replacement cost of the assets that affect the quality of the product regularly assessed?

4. How does the financial policy and budget support the training and development of personnel?

5. What is the policy and practice regarding payment of suppliers to support mutuality and continuity of supply?

6. How are the costs of Quality and Non Conformance regularly measured?

7. How are the costs of Quality and Non Conformance regularly reported and analysed?

8. How are the costs of Quality and Non Conformance regularly communicated throughout the organization?

9. What methods are used to benchmark the performance of key financial measures including Quality costs, creditor days and training expenditure?

10. What methods are used to systematically manage improvement of financial parameters?

Financial review and improvement

Achievement financial objectives

The purpose in examining the achievement of financial objectives is to establish that:

a) the organization is using soundly based methods for their accomplishment

b) the organizational objectives are being achieved

c) the organization has the financial resources necessary to produce products and services that satisfy customer needs and expectations.

1. What measures are used to verify achievement of the financial objectives and what target values have been agreed?

2. How are the results of measurement captured?

3. What results are being achieved?

4. What methods of measurement are used and how often are measurements taken?

5. What methods are used to ensure the integrity of these measurements?

6. How are the results conveyed to those responsible for taking action?

7. What analysis has been performed to determine the cause of the difference between actual and planned results?

8. What improvement in results was obtained from the last review of the finance process?

Finance process effectiveness

The purpose in examining the effectiveness of the finance process is to establish that the best ways of achieving the objectives are being used.

1. What checks are used to verify that the manner in which the finance process is implemented is consistent with the organization's policies and values?

2. What checks are used to verify the activities being carried out are best practice?

3. How is best practice defined?

4. What methods are used to conduct these checks and how often are they performed?

5. Who is involved in this assessment?

6. How are the results of this assessment captured?

7. How are these results conveyed to those responsible for taking action?

8. What improvement in effectiveness was obtained when the finance process was last reviewed?

9. How was this improvement measured?

Relevance of financial policies and objectives

The purpose in examining the relevance of financial policy and objectives is to establish that the organization has in place soundly based methods to improve alignment of these goals with the corporate policy.

1. What checks are carried out to verify that the financial objectives remain relevant to the achievement of the organization's corporate policy and objectives?

2. What methods are used to conduct these checks and how often are they performed?

3. Who is involved in this review?

4. How are the results of this review captured?

5. What methods are used to ensure the integrity of this information?

6. How are the results conveyed to those responsible for taking action?

7. What action was taken the last time these checks were performed that resulted in a change to the financial policies and objectives?

Human resource management process

Process description

Triggered by the organization's objectives and requirements of specific customers, projects and initiatives, the human resource management process identifies, acquires, maintains and develops the human resources needed to fulfil its objectives.

Human Resource Management policies and objectives

The purpose in examining human resource policies and objectives is to establish that the effort is focused on delivering competent resources in order to achieve the organization's corporate policies and objectives.

1. What is the purpose of the human resource management process?
2. What is the human resource policy of the organization?
3. How does this policy relate to the organization's corporate policy?
4. What are the human resource objectives for the organization?
5. What is the process by which these objectives are established?
6. How do these objectives relate to the organizational goals and the human resource policy?
7. How are the human resource policies and objectives communicated throughout the organization?
8. How is understanding of these policies and objectives confirmed?

Human Resource activities

The purpose in examining human resource activities is to establish that the organization's methods for acquiring, deploying and developing the organization's human resources are soundly based.

Generic

1. What are the key stages in the process that have been established for achieving the human resource objectives?
2. What specific outputs are required from each stage in the human resource management process?

3. What analysis has been carried out to determine the factors that affect accomplishment of stage outputs?

4. How have the results of this analysis been reflected in the design of the human resource process?

5. How do you know the process is capable of achieving the required human resource objectives?

6. What specific measures are used to monitor successful achievement of these outputs?

7. What are the measurable targets for each of these key stages?

8. What methods of measurement are used and how often are measurements taken?

9. How is the integrity of the method of measurement maintained to ensure consistency of measurement?

10. How are the results of measurement captured?

11. How are the results of measurement conveyed to those responsible for taking action?

12. What action was taken the last time these checks were performed that resulted in improved stage output?

13. What information in the human resource management process is necessary for each stage to be performed as planned?

14. How is this information communicated to the staff who perform the planned human resource activities?

15. How is the currency, validity and integrity of this information maintained?

16. How do you know that the human resource activities are being performed as planned?

17. What action is carried out when human resource activities are not performed as planned?

Specific

1. How are the responsibilities within each role defined and assigned to the roles in the organization structure?

2. What analysis has been carried out to optimise the relationships, roles, responsibility and authority within the organization structure?

3. How are the HR requirements to fulfil the objectives determined?

4. How do the defined responsibilities and requirements for each role link to achieving organizational objectives?

5. How are the factors that directly impact on customer satisfaction defined in the responsibilities and requirements?

6. How is the timely need for new and replacement roles defined?

7. How does the recruitment and selection process ensure that defined requirements for new and transferred staff are met?

8. How are requirements communicated to external recruitment providers for effective recruitment?

9. What is the process for carrying out skills assessment, taking into account current capability and needs based upon future business objectives?

10. How does the process for induction of new and transferred staff ensure that factors that affect customer satisfaction are understood?

11. What is the process for identifying training and development for all staff?

12. How are training and development needs translated into competences?

13. How are the standards for these competences defined and performance against these standards evaluated?

14. What is the process for providing training and development?

15. How has the process for providing training and development been validated prior to commencement?

16. How is the effectiveness of the training and development evaluated with respect to improved individual and organizational performance?

17. How are the results of evaluating the process of training and development provision used in improving future provision?

18. What is the process for identifying additional training requirements resulting from changes in customer, statutory and regulatory requirements or internal standards, new products and services, new or modified equipment?

19. What methods are used to maintain information regarding current competence of staff?

20. What process is in place to measure staff satisfaction?

21. How does this take into account the reasons why people leave the organization?

22. What process is used for succession planning to ensure continuing capability?

23. What methods are used to ensure effective two-way communication within the organization?

24. What process is in place to encourage innovation and improvement suggestions from staff?

Human resource review and improvement

Achievement of human resource objectives

The purpose in examining the achievement of human resource policies and objectives is to establish that:

a) the organization is using soundly based methods for their accomplishment

b) the organizational policies and objectives are being achieved

c) the organization has the human resources necessary to supply products and services that satisfy customer needs and expectations.

1. What measures are used to verify achievement of the human resource objectives and what target values have been agreed?

2. How are the results of measurement captured?

3. What results are being achieved?

4. What methods of measurement are used and how often are measurements taken?

5. What methods are used to ensure the integrity of these measurements?

6. How are the results conveyed to those responsible for taking action?

7. What analysis has been performed to determine the cause of the difference between actual and planned results?

8. What improvement in results was obtained from the last review of the human resource process?

Human resource process effectiveness

The purpose in examining the effectiveness of the human resource process is to establish that the best ways of achieving the objectives are being used.

1. What checks are used to verify that the manner in which the human resource process is implemented is consistent with the organization's policies and values?

2. What checks are used to verify the activities being carried out are best practice?

3. How is best practice defined?

4. What methods are used to conduct these checks and how often are they performed?

5. Who is involved in this assessment?

6. How are the results of this assessment captured?

7. How are these results conveyed to those responsible for taking action?

8. What improvement in effectiveness was obtained when the human resource process was last reviewed?

9. How was this improvement measured?

Relevance of human resource policies and objectives

The purpose in examining the relevance of human resource policy and objectives is to establish that the organization has in place soundly based methods to improve alignment of these goals with the corporate policy.

1. What checks are carried out to verify that the human resource objectives remain relevant to the achievement of the organization's corporate policy and objectives?

2. What methods are used to conduct these checks and how often are they performed?

3. Who is involved in this review?

4. How are the results of this review captured?

5. What methods are used to ensure the integrity of this information?

6. How are the results conveyed to those responsible for taking action?

7. What action was taken the last time these checks were performed that resulted in a change to the human resource policies and objectives?

Purchasing process

Process description

Triggered by the organization's objectives and requirements of specific customers, projects and initiatives, the purchasing process identifies and acquires, physical resources needed to fulfil its objectives.

Purchasing policies and objectives

The purpose in examining purchasing policies and objectives is to establish that the effort used to acquire the organization's physical resources is focused on building mutually beneficial relationships with suppliers and consistent with the organization's corporate policies and objectives.

1. What is the purpose of the purchasing process?
2. What is the purchasing policy of the organization?
3. How does this policy relate to the organization's corporate policy?
4. What are the objectives for the supply of materials, components, buildings and equipment?
5. What is the process by which these objectives are established?
6. How do these objectives relate to the organizational goals and the purchasing policy?
7. How are the purchasing policies and objectives conveyed throughout the organization?
8. How is understanding of these policies and objectives confirmed?

Purchasing activities

The purpose in examining purchasing activities is to establish that the organization's methods for the identification and acquisition of physical resources are soundly based.

Generic
1. What are the key stages in the process that have been established for achieving the purchasing objectives?
2. What specific outputs are required from each stage in the purchasing process?

3. What analysis has been carried out to determine the factors that affect accomplishment of stage outputs?

4. How have the results of this analysis been reflected in the design of the purchasing process?

5. How do you know the process is capable of achieving the required purchasing objectives?

6. What specific measures are used to monitor successful achievement of these outputs?

7. What are the measurable targets for each of these key stages?

8. What methods of measurement are used and how often are measurements taken?

9. How is the integrity of the method of measurement maintained to ensure consistency of measurement?

10. How are the results of measurement captured?

11. How are the results of measurement conveyed to those responsible for taking action?

12. What action was taken the last time these checks were performed that resulted in improved stage output?

13. What information in the purchasing process is necessary for each stage to be performed as planned?

14. How is this information communicated to the staff who perform the planned purchasing activities?

15. How is the currency, validity and integrity of this information maintained?

16. How do you know that the purchasing activities are being performed as planned?

17. What action is carried out when purchasing activities are not performed as planned?

Specific

1. What inputs trigger the purchasing process and from where do they originate?

2. How do you determine the activities needed to ensure specific purchases meet the organization's requirements?

3. How do you determine the resources needed to manage the acquisition of physical resources?

4. How do you determine the requirements for purchased products or services?

5. How do you determine the relevant statutory and regulator requirements that impact the purchasing of goods and services?

6. What analysis has been carried out to determine potential sources of supply of external resources needed to meet the purchasing objectives?

7. How did you establish that these resources are capable of providing product of the right quality on time economically?

8. How are risks to meeting the purchasing objectives identified and managed?

9. How have those requiring purchased products and services been involved in their acquisition?

10. What actions are taken to ensure purchasing proceeds with an agreed set of requirements?

11. How is purchasing information communicated to the suppliers?

12. How do you ensure that suppliers understand purchasing information?

13. How do you maintain the currency, validity and integrity of the purchasing information?

14. What information is necessary for each stage to be performed as planned?

15. How is this information communicated to the staff who perform the planned activities?

16. How is the currency, validity and integrity of this information maintained?

17. What controls are in place to ensure that the activities are performed as planned?

18. What action is carried out when activities are not performed as planned?

Purchasing review and improvement

Achievement of purchasing objectives

The purpose in examining the achievement of purchasing objectives is to establish that:

a)   the organization is using soundly based methods for their accomplishment

b)   the organizational objectives are being achieved

c)   the organization is purchasing products and services that satisfy its requirements.

   1.   What measures are used to verify achievement of the purchasing objectives and what target values have been agreed?

   2.   What specific measures are used to verify that the purchased products and services meet the organization's requirements?

   3.   How are the results of measurement captured?

   4.   What results are being achieved?

   5.   What methods of measurement are used and how often are measurements taken?

   6.   What methods are used to ensure the integrity of these measurements?

   7.   How are the results conveyed to those responsible for taking action?

   8.   What analysis has been performed to determine the cause of the difference between actual and planned results?

   9.   What improvement in results was obtained from the last review of the purchasing process?

Purchasing process effectiveness

The purpose in examining the effectiveness of the purchasing process is to establish that the best ways of achieving the objectives are being used.

   1.   What checks are used to verify that the manner in which the purchasing process is implemented is consistent with the organization's policies and values?

   2.   What checks are used to verify the activities being carried out are best practice?

3. How is best practice defined?

4. What methods are used to conduct these checks and how often are they performed?

5. Who is involved in this verification?

6. How are the results of this verification captured?

7. How are these results conveyed to those responsible for taking action?

8. What improvement in effectiveness was obtained when the purchasing process was last reviewed?

9. How was this improvement measured?

Relevance of purchasing policies and objectives

The purpose in examining the relevance of purchasing policy and objectives is to establish that the organization has in place soundly based methods to improve alignment of these goals with the corporate policy.

1. What checks are carried out to verify that the purchasing objectives remain relevant to the achievement of the organization's corporate policy and objectives?

2. What methods are used to conduct these checks and how often are they performed?

3. Who is involved in this review?

4. How are the results of this review captured?

5. What methods are used to ensure the integrity of this information?

6. How are the results conveyed to those responsible for taking action?

7. What action was taken the last time these checks were performed that resulted in a change to the purchasing policies and objectives?

Physical resource maintenance process

Process description

Triggered by the organization's objectives and requirements of specific customers, projects and initiatives, the resource maintenance process maintains the physical resources needed to fulfil its objectives.

Resource maintenance policies and objectives

The purpose in examining resource maintenance policies and objectives is to establish that the effort used to maintain the organization's physical resources is focused on enabling the organization to satisfy the needs of interested parties and achieve its goals.

1. What is the purpose of the resource maintenance process?
2. What is the resource maintenance policy of the organization?
3. How does this policy relate to the organization's corporate policy?
4. What are the objectives for the maintenance of buildings, plant and equipment?
5. What is the process by which these objectives are established?
6. How do these objectives relate to the organizational goals and the resource maintenance policy?
7. How are the resource maintenance policies and objectives conveyed throughout the organization?
8. How is understanding of these policies and objectives confirmed?

Resource maintenance activities

The purpose in examining resource maintenance activities is to establish that the organization's methods for the maintenance of physical resources are soundly based.

Generic
1. What are the key stages in the process that have been established for achieving the resource maintenance objectives?
2. What specific outputs are required from each stage in the resource maintenance process?

3. What analysis has been carried out to determine the factors that affect accomplishment of stage outputs?

4. How have the results of this analysis been reflected in the design of the resource maintenance process?

5. How do you know that the process is capable of achieving the required resource maintenance objectives?

6. What specific measures are used to monitor successful achievement of these outputs?

7. What are the measurable targets for each of these key stages?

8. What methods of measurement are used and how often are measurements taken?

9. How is the integrity of the method of measurement maintained to ensure consistency of measurement?

10. How are the results of measurement captured?

11. How are the results of measurements conveyed to those responsible for taking action?

12. What action was taken the last time these checks were performed that resulted in improved stage output?

13. What information in the resource maintenance process is necessary for each stage to be performed as planned?

14. How is this information communicated to the staff who perform the planned resource maintenance activities?

15. How is the currency, validity and integrity of this information maintained?

16. How do you know that the resource maintenance activities are being performed as planned?

17. What action is carried out when resource maintenance activities are not performed as planned?

Specific

1. What inputs trigger the corrective and preventive maintenance processes and from where do they originate?

2. How do you determine the type, depth and frequency of resource maintenance necessary to prevent deterioration in serviceability standards?

3. How are risks to meeting the resource maintenance objectives identified and managed?

4. How do you determine the relevant statutory and regulatory requirements that impact the maintenance of equipment, buildings and facilities?

5. How do you determine the resources needed to maintain the physical resources?

6. How have those using the physical resources been involved in planning their maintenance?

7. What actions are taken to ensure resource maintenance proceeds with an agreed set of requirements?

8. How are resource maintenance requirements communicated to those responsible for maintaining the organization's physical resources?

9. How do you ensure that these personnel understand resource maintenance requirements?

10. How do you maintain the currency, validity and integrity of the resource maintenance requirements?

11. What information is necessary for each stage to be performed as planned?

12. How is this information communicated to the staff who perform the planned activities?

13. How is the currency, validity and integrity of this information maintained?

Resource maintenance review and improvement

Achievement of resource maintenance objectives

The purpose in examining the achievement of resource maintenance objectives is to establish that:

a) the organization is using soundly based methods for their accomplishment

b) the organizational objectives are being achieved

c) the organization is maintaining products and services in a condition that fulfils its operational requirements.

1. What measures are used to verify achievement of the resource maintenance objectives and what target values have been agreed?

2. How are the results of measurement captured?

3. What results are being achieved?

4. What methods of measurement are used and how often are measurements taken?

5. What methods are used to ensure the integrity of these measurements?

6. How are the results conveyed to those responsible for taking action?

7. What analysis has been performed to determine the cause of the difference between actual and planned results?

8. What improvement in business continuity was obtained from the last review of the resource maintenance process?

Resource maintenance process effectiveness

The purpose in examining the effectiveness of the resource maintenance process is to establish that the best ways of achieving the objectives are being used.

1. What checks are used to verify that the manner in which the resource maintenance process is implemented is consistent with the organization's policies and values?

2. What checks are used to verify the activities being carried out are best practice?

3. How is best practice defined?

4. What methods are used to conduct these checks and how often are they performed?

5. Who is involved in this assessment?

6. How are the results of this assessment captured?

7. How are these results conveyed to those responsible for taking action?

8. What improvement in effectiveness was obtained when the resource maintenance process was last reviewed?

9. How was this improvement measured?

Relevance of resource maintenance policies and objectives

The purpose in examining the relevance of resource maintenance policy and objectives is to establish that the organization has in place soundly based methods to improve alignment of these goals with the corporate policy.

1. What checks are carried out to verify that the resource maintenance objectives remain relevant to the achievement of the organization's corporate policy and objectives?

2. What methods are used to conduct these checks and how often are they performed?

3. Who is involved in this review?

4. How are the results of this review captured?

5. What methods are used to ensure the integrity of this information?

6. How are the results conveyed to those responsible for taking action?

7. What action was taken the last time these checks were performed that resulted in a change to the resource maintenance policies and objectives?

Product development process

Process description

For the purpose of this book the product development process transforms customer needs and expectations or specified requirements into products and services that satisfy customers. For new products/services, the requirements pass through a design process before emerging as a set of proven specifications that can be transformed into a tangible product/service. There are many variations within this process depending on the nature of the transaction between customer and supplier.

Product development policies and objectives

The purpose in examining product development goals is to establish that the development effort is focused on creating product features that serve the needs and expectations of external stakeholders and are consistent with the organization's corporate policies and objectives.

1. What is the purpose of the product development process?
2. What is the product development policy of the organization?
3. How does this policy relate to the organization's corporate policy?
4. What are the product development objectives for the organization?
5. What is the process by which these objectives are established?
6. How do these objectives relate to the organizational goals and the product development policy?
7. How are the product development policies and objectives conveyed throughout the organization?
8. How is understanding of these policies and objectives confirmed?

Product development activities

The purpose in examining the product development activities is to establish that the organization has the intent and capability to develop products consistent with the identified market needs.

Generic

1. What are the key stages in the process that have been established for achieving the product development objectives?

2. What specific outputs are required from each stage in the product development process?

3. What analysis has been carried out to determine the factors that affect accomplishment of stage outputs?

4. How have the results of this analysis been reflected in the design of the product development process?

5. How do you know the process is capable of achieving the required product development objectives?

6. What specific measures are used to monitor successful achievement of these outputs?

7. What are the measurable targets for each of these key stages?

8. What methods of measurement are used and how often are measurements taken?

9. How is the integrity of the method of measurement maintained to ensure consistency of measurement?

10. How are the results of measurement captured?

11. How are the results of measurements conveyed to those responsible for taking action?

12. What action was taken the last time these checks were performed that resulted in improved stage output?

13. What information in the product development process is necessary for each stage to be performed as planned?

14. How is this information communicated to the staff who perform the planned product development activities?

15. How is the currency, validity and integrity of this information maintained?

16. How do you know that the product development activities are being performed as planned?

17. What action is carried out when product development activities are not performed as planned?

Specific

1. What inputs trigger specific product development and from where do they originate?

2. How do you determine the requirements the product needs to satisfy to meet the needs and expectations of customers?

3. What analysis has been carried out to determine the current and future technologies, competences and resources needed to meet the product development objectives?

4. How do you determine the relevant statutory and regulatory requirements that impact the design?

5. How did you determine the current and future resources necessary to acquire the necessary design capability?

6. How do you determine the activities needed to develop specific design solutions?

7. How do you determine the resources required to produce successful designs?

8. How are risks to meeting the design objectives identified and managed?

9. What are the criteria for deciding how work is allocated?

10. How are work assignments conveyed to those concerned?

11. What plans have been developed to achieve the product development objectives?

12. How is the integrity of this information maintained throughout development?

13. How have those impacted by these plans been involved in their development?

14. What actions are taken to ensure development proceeds with an agreed set of requirements?

Product development review and improvement

Achievement of product development objectives

The purpose in examining the achievement of product development objectives is to establish that:

a) the organization is using soundly based methods for their accomplishment

b) the organizational policies and objectives are being achieved

c) the organization is developing products and services that the marketing process indicates are needed to satisfy customer needs and expectations.

   1. What measures are used to verify achievement of the product development objectives?

   2. What specific measures are used to verify that designs meet customer requirements and are capable of economic realization using currently available facilities?

   3. How are the results of measurement captured?

   4. What results are being achieved?

   5. What method of measurement is used and how often are measurements taken?

   6. What methods are used to ensure the integrity of these measurements?

   7. How are the results conveyed to those responsible for taking action?

   8. What analysis has been performed to determine the cause of the difference between actual and planned results?

   9. What improvement in results was obtained from the last review of the product development process?

Product development process effectiveness

The purpose in examining the effectiveness of the product development process is to establish that the best ways of achieving the objectives are being used.

   1. What checks are used to verify that the manner in which the product development process is implemented is consistent with the organization's policies and values?

   2. What checks are used to verify the activities being carried out are best practice?

   3. How is best practice defined?

   4. What methods are used to conduct these checks and how often are they performed?

5. Who is involved in this assessment?

6. How are the results of this assessment captured?

7. How are these results conveyed to those responsible for taking action?

8. What improvement in effectiveness was obtained when the product development process was last reviewed?

9. How was this improvement measured?

Relevance of product development policies and objectives

The purpose in examining the relevance of product development policy and objectives is to establish that the organization has in place soundly based methods to improve alignment of these goals with the corporate policy.

1. What checks are carried out to verify that the product development objectives remain relevant to the achievement of the organization's corporate policy and objectives?

2. What methods are used to conduct these checks and how often are they performed?

3. Who is involved in this review?

4. How are the results of this review captured?

5. What methods are used to ensure the integrity of this information?

6. How are the results conveyed to those responsible for taking action?

7. What action was taken the last time these checks were performed that resulted in a change to the product development policies and objectives?

Production process

Process description

For the purpose of this book the production process replicates proven designs to consistent standards. There are many variations within this process depending on the nature of the product. The process is triggered either by the sales process or the product development process.

Production policies and objectives

The purpose in examining production policy and objectives is to establish that they are consistent with the organization's corporate policies and objectives.

1. What is the purpose of the production process?
2. What is the production policy of the organization?
3. How does this policy relate to the organization's corporate policy?
4. What are the production objectives for the organization?
5. What is the process by which these objectives are established?
6. How do these objectives relate to the organizational objectives?
7. How are the production policies and objectives communicated throughout the organization?
8. How is understanding of these policies and objectives confirmed?

Production activities

The purpose in examining production goals is to establish that the production effort is focused on producing products that conform to proven designs in a manner that is consistent with the organization's corporate policies and objectives.

Generic
1. What are the key stages in the process that have been established for achieving the production objectives?
2. What specific outputs are required from each stage in the production process?
3. What analysis has been carried out to determine the factors that affect accomplishment of stage outputs?

4. How have the results of this analysis been reflected in the design of the production process?

5. How do you know that the process is capable of achieving the required production objectives?

6. What specific measures are used to monitor successful achievement of these outputs?

7. What are the measurable targets for each of these key stages?

8. What methods of measurement are used and how often are measurements taken?

9. How is the integrity of the method of measurement maintained to ensure consistency of measurement?

10. How are the results of measurement captured?

11. How are the results of measurements conveyed to those responsible for taking action?

12. What action was taken the last time these checks were performed that resulted in improved stage output?

13. What information in the production process is necessary for each stage to be performed as planned?

14. How is this information communicated to the staff who perform the planned production activities?

15. How is the currency, validity and integrity of this information maintained?

16. How do you know that the production activities are being performed as planned?

17. What action is carried out when production activities are not performed as planned?

Specific

1. What is the process for ensuring that the right quantity of products is produced at the right time while optimising the utilization of production resources?

2. What analysis is performed to identify the constraints in the production flow?

3. How are the results of this analysis used to overcome bottlenecks in production?

4. What is the process for determining the sequence of operations needed to produce product?

5. What criteria are used to determine the stages at which product verification is needed?

6. What methods are used to establish that work processes can deliver conforming product before being activated?

7. How do you prevent substandard product from entering the production flow?

8. How do you ensure waste product is disposed of in accordance with the governing regulations?

Production review and improvement

Achievement of production objectives

The purpose in examining the achievement of production objectives is to establish that:

a) the organization is using soundly based methods for their accomplishment

b) the organizational policies and objectives are being achieved

c) the organization is producing products that satisfy customer needs and expectations.

1. What measures are used to verify achievement of the production policies and objectives?

2. What specific measures are used to verify that designs meet customer requirements and are capable of economic realization using currently available facilities?

3. How are the results of measurement captured?

4. What results are being achieved?

5. What method of measurement is used and how often are measurements taken?

6. What methods are used to ensure the integrity of these measurements?

7. How are the results conveyed to those responsible for taking action?

8. What analysis has been performed to determine the cause of the difference between actual and planned results?

9. What improvement in results was obtained from the last review of the production process?

Production process effectiveness

The purpose in examining the effectiveness of the production process is to establish that the best ways of achieving the objectives are being employed.

1. What checks are used to verify that the manner in which the production process is implemented is consistent with the organization's policies and values?

2. What checks are used to verify the activities being carried out are best practice?

3. How is best practice defined?

4. What methods are used to conduct these checks and how often are they performed?

5. Who is involved in this assessment?

6. How are the results of this assessment captured?

7. How are these results conveyed to those responsible for taking action?

8. What improvement in effectiveness was obtained when the production process was last reviewed?

9. How was this improvement measured?

Relevance of production policies and objectives

The purpose in examining the relevance of production policy and objectives is to establish that the organization has in place soundly based methods to improve alignment of these goals with the corporate policy.

1. What checks are carried out to verify that the production objectives remain relevant to the achievement of the organization's corporate policy and objectives?

2. What methods are used to conduct these checks and how often are they performed?

3. Who is involved in this review?

4. How are the results of this review captured?

5. What methods are used to ensure the integrity of this information?

6. How are the results conveyed to those responsible for taking action?

7. What action was taken the last time these checks were performed that resulted in a change to the production policies and objectives?

Distribution process

Process description

For the purpose of this book the distribution process supplies saleable product against customer orders. In some cases the product may be in stock or is shipped directly from the production line through wholesalers and retailers before reaching the end user. This process would include sub-processes of storage, packing, dispatch, shipment and invoicing. Installation is considered a service and therefore included in service delivery.

Distribution policies and objectives

The purpose in examining distribution policy and objectives is to establish that they are consistent with the organization's corporate policies and objectives.

1. What is the purpose of the distribution process?
2. What is the distribution policy of the organization?
3. How does this policy relate to the organizations corporate policy?
4. What are the distribution objectives for the organization?
5. What is the process by which these objectives are established?
6. How do these objectives relate to the organization's goals and the distribution policy?
7. How are the distribution policies and objectives communicated throughout the organization?
8. How is understanding of these policies and objectives confirmed?

Distribution Activities

The purpose in examining distribution activities is to establish that the organization's methods for distributing product achieve customer satisfaction and meets the organizational objectives.

Generic
1. What are the key stages in the process that have been established for achieving the distribution objectives?
2. What specific outputs are required from each stage in the distribution process?

3. What analysis ha been carried out to determine the factors that affect accomplishment of stage outputs?

4. How have the results of this analysis been reflected in the design of the distribution process?

5. How do you know the process is capable of achieving the required distribution objectives?

6. What specific measures are used to monitor successful achievement of these outputs?

7. What are the measurable targets for each of these key stages?

8. What methods of measurement are used and how often are measurements taken?

9. How is the integrity of the method of measurement maintained to ensure consistency of measurement?

10. How are the results of measurement captured?

11. How are the results of measurements conveyed to those responsible for taking action?

12. What action was taken the last time these checks were performed that resulted in improved stage output?

13. What information in the distribution process is necessary for each stage to be performed as planned?

14. How is this information communicated to the staff who perform the planned distribution activities?

15. How is the currency, validity and integrity of this information maintained?

16. How do you know that the distribution activities are being performed as planned?

17. What action is carried out when distribution activities are not performed as planned?

Specific

1. What inputs trigger product distribution and from where do they originate?

2. How do you determine the handling, storage, packing and transportation requirements that will prevent deterioration of specific products during distribution?

3. How do you ensure that appropriate product handling features are accommodated into product design and manufacture?

4. How do you determine the relevant statutory and regulatory requirements that impact the distribution of product?

5. How do you determine the activities needed to meet the distribution requirements?

6. How did you determine the current and future resources necessary to distribute product?

7. How are risks to meeting the distribution requirements identified and managed?

8. What are the criteria for deciding how work is allocated?

9. How are work assignments conveyed to those concerned?

10. What plans have been developed to achieve distribution objectives?

11. How is the integrity of this information maintained throughout the distribution process?

12. How have those impacted by these plans been involved in their development?

13. What actions are taken to ensure distribution proceeds with an agreed set of requirements?

Distribution review and improvement

Achievement of distribution objectives

The purpose in examining the achievement of distribution objectives is to establish that:

a) the organization is using soundly based methods for their accomplishment

b) the organizational objectives are being achieved

c) the organization is providing a distribution service that satisfies customer needs and expectations.

1. What measures are used to verify achievement of the distribution objectives and what target values have been agreed?

2. What specific measures are used to verify that customers receive products on time and in good condition?

3. How are the results of measurement captured?

4. What results are being achieved?

5. What method of measurement is used and how often are measurements taken?

6. How are the results conveyed to those responsible for taking action?

7. What methods are used to ensure the integrity of these measurements?

8. What analysis has been performed to determine the cause of the difference between actual and planned results?

9. What improvement in results was obtained from the last review of the distribution process?

Distribution process effectiveness

The purpose in examining the effectiveness of the distribution process is to establish that the best ways of achieving the objectives are being used.

1. What checks are used to verify that the manner in which the distribution process is implemented is consistent with the organization's policies and values?

2. What checks are used to verify the activities being carried out are best practice?

3. How is best practice defined?

4. What methods are used to conduct these checks and how often are they performed?

5. Who is involved in this assessment?

6. How are the results of this assessment captured?

7. How are these results conveyed to those responsible for taking action?

8. What improvement in effectiveness was obtained when the distribution process was last reviewed?

9. How was this improvement measured?

Relevance of distribution policies and objectives

The purpose in examining achievement of the distribution policies and objectives is to establish that the organization reviews the relevance of these and has in place soundly based methods to improve alignment of these goals with the corporate policy.

1. What checks are carried out to verify that the objectives set for the distribution remain relevant to the achievement of the organization's corporate policy and objectives?

2. What methods are used to conduct these checks and how often are they performed?

3. Who is involved in this review?

4. How are the results of this review captured?

5. What methods are used to ensure the integrity of this information?

6. How are the results conveyed to those responsible for taking action?

7. What action was taken last time these checks were performed that resulted in a change to the distribution policies and objectives?

Service delivery process

Process description

For the purpose of this book the service delivery process delivers a proven service design to consistent standards. For existing services, this process would involve the pre-service delivery processes such as planning. There are many variations within this process depending on the nature of the service therefore only a general outline can be represented by these questions.

Service delivery policies and objectives

The purpose in examining service delivery policy and objectives is to establish that they are consistent with the organization's corporate policies and objectives.

1. What is the purpose of the service delivery process?
2. What is the service delivery policy of the organization?
3. How does this policy relate to the organizations corporate policy?
4. What are the service delivery objectives for the organization?
5. How have those responsible for achieving these objectives been involved in their development?
6. How do these objectives relate to the organizational objectives?
7. How are the service delivery policies and objectives communicated throughout the organization?
8. How is understanding of these policies and objectives confirmed?

Service delivery activities

The purpose in examining service delivery activities is to establish that the organization's methods for providing the promised service to the customer achieves customer satisfaction and meets the organizational objectives.

Generic

1. What are the key stages in the process that have been established for achieving the service delivery objectives?
2. What specific outputs are required from each stage of the service delivery process?

3. What analysis has been carried out to determine the factors that affect accomplishment of stage outputs?

4. How have the results of this analysis been reflected in the design of the service delivery process?

5. How do you know that the process is capable of achieving the required service delivery objectives?

6. What specific measures are used to monitor successful achievement of these outputs?

7. What are the measurable targets for each of these key stages?

8. What methods of measurement are used and how often are measurements taken?

9. How is the integrity of the method of measurement maintained to ensure consistency of measurement?

10. How are the results of the measurement captured?

11. How are the results of measurements conveyed to those responsible for taking action?

12. What action was taken the last time these checks were performed that resulted in improved stage output?

13. What information in the service delivery process is necessary for each stage to be performed as planned?

14. How is this information communicated to the staff who perform the planned service delivery activities?

15. How is the currency, validity and integrity of this information maintained?

16. How do you know that the service delivery activities are being performed as planned?

17. What action is carried out when service delivery activities are not performed as planned?

Specific

1. What inputs trigger service delivery and from where do they originate?

2. How is the anticipated demand on the service delivery process forecasted?

3. How do you determine the current and future resources necessary to meet the forecasted demand?

4. What action is taken when demand exceeds current resources?

5. How are risks to meeting the service delivery requirements identified and managed?

6. What methods are employed to ensure continuity of service in the event of equipment malfunction or supplier default?

7. What are the criteria for deciding how work is allocated?

8. How are work assignments conveyed to those concerned?

9. What plans have been developed to achieve service delivery objectives?

10. How is the integrity of this information maintained throughout the service delivery process?

11. How have those impacted by these plans been involved in their development?

12. What actions are taken to ensure service delivery proceeds with an agreed set of requirements?

Service delivery review and improvement

Achievement of service delivery objectives

The purpose in examining the measurement of service delivery objectives is to establish that:

a) the organization is using soundly based methods for their accomplishment

b) the organizational objectives are being achieved

c) the organization is providing services that satisfy customer needs and expectations.

1. What measures are used to verify achievement of the service delivery objectives and what target values have been agreed?

2. What specific measures are used to verify that the organization's services meet customer needs and expectations?

3. How are the results of measuring customer satisfaction captured?

4. What results are being achieved?

5. What method of measurement is used and how often are measurements taken?

6. What methods are used to ensure the integrity of these measurements?

7. How are the results conveyed to those responsible for taking action?

8. What analysis has been performed to determine the cause of the difference between actual and planned results?

9. What improvement in results was obtained from the last review of the service delivery process?

Service delivery process effectiveness

The purpose in examining the effectiveness of the service delivery process is to establish that the best ways of achieving the objectives are being used.

1. What checks are used to verify that the manner in which the service delivery process is implemented is consistent with the organization's policies and values?

2. What checks are used to verify the activities being carried out are best practice?

3. How is best practice defined?

4. What methods are used to conduct these checks and how often are they performed?

5. Who is involved in this assessment?

6. How are the results of this assessment captured?

7. How are these results conveyed to those responsible for taking action?

8. What improvement in effectiveness was obtained when the service delivery process was last reviewed?

9. How was this improvement measured?

Relevance of service delivery policies and objectives

The purpose in examining achievement of the service delivery policies and objectives is to establish that the organization reviews the relevance of these and has in place soundly based methods to improve alignment of these goals with the corporate policy.

1. What checks are carried out to verify that the objectives set for the service delivery remain relevant to the achievement of the organization's corporate policy and objectives?

2. What methods are used to conduct these checks and how often are they performed?

3. Who is involved in this review?

4. How are the results of this review captured?

5. What methods are used to ensure the integrity of this information?

6. How are the results conveyed to those responsible for taking action?

7. What action was taken last time these checks were performed that resulted in a change to the service delivery policies and objectives?

Chapter 9

Conclusions

At the beginning of this book we set out to introduce a new approach to auditing; an approach that would produce results that attract the attention of management because it is aligned with their real purpose – to improve the organization's capability to satisfy its customers and other interested parties.

Various approaches to auditing were analysed and shown as contributing little to the organization's need to remain competitive. Clearly a more effective auditing methodology was needed - one that focused on performance and not on conformity – one that took a more strategic and objective approach, rather than one that focused on tasks and rules, independent of objectives. The new approach – *the process approach*, was introduced as an effective way forward. The importance of the 8 Quality management principles was stressed and used to support the new approach and show how they were expressed within the requirements of ISO 9001.

The process approach is characterised by five key, simple but powerful questions from which all others are derived:

Q1   *What are you trying to do?*

Q2   *How do you make it happen?*

Q3   *How do you know you are doing it right?*

Q4   *How do you know it's the best way of doing it?*

Q5   *How do you know it's the right thing to do?*

These questions were applied at three organizational levels:

Enterprise level

Managerial level

Operational level

This resulted in a series of questions that could take an auditor on a journey from the organization's mission to the individual's contribution, through policies, objectives, measures, processes, results and continual improvement - a journey that identifies the clear linkages between the interconnected processes, where the requirements of the Standard fit with the processes and where application of the Quality management principles can be demonstrated.

The process approach is a radical new approach, it eliminates many of the weaknesses of previous approaches and provides an effective technique that will enable auditors to establish that an organization is really managing its processes effectively.

Appendix A

Aligning processes to requirements

The purpose of this Appendix is to show how the questions contained in Chapter 5 generate the evidence needed to demonstrate compliance with the requirements of ISO 9001. The questions contained in Chapter 5 were designed to establish that the organization's processes are being managed effectively. ISO 9001 contains requirements which if met should enable organizations to satisfy their customers but it was not intended as a definitive guide to managing an organization. There are therefore many aspects of management that are not included in ISO 9001. The traditional approach to auditing as explained in Chapter 3 has been to either use requirements to guide the questions and the sequence in which they are asked or to map the requirements onto a department and again use requirements to guide the questions and the sequence in which they are asked. In the first case, requirements would be addressed only once and in the latter case, they would be addressed in every department to which they were applicable. It is still however an ineffective method of determining whether an organization is managing its processes effectively - which is the fundamental reason for conducting the audits.

Some requirements of ISO 9001 are generic and apply to all processes and others are only applicable to specific processes. However, the identity of which requirements are generic is not always obvious. For example the requirements for internal communication in clause 5.5.3 and those for objectives in clause 5.4.1, apply to all processes. Section 8 on monitoring, measurement, analysis and improvement applies to all processes but monitoring and measurement are also addressed by the clauses on design verification and validation in section 7.3, verification of purchased material in clause 7.4.3 and management review in clause 5.6. The generic requirements in clause 4.1 are amplified by the requirements in sections, 5, 6, 7 & 8 but not in the same order or under headings that match the requirements. Section 6 on resource management addresses the human and physical resource requirements but the requirements applying to financial resources are included in the generic requirement of clause 6.1. (Appendix B shows how all the clauses relate to the requirements of clause 4.1).

It is therefore difficult to plan effective audits using the structure of ISO 9001 as the model. A more effective way to plan an audit is to identify the business processes of the organization and assess these using the questions identified in Chapters 5, 6 & 7. In order to provide added confidence that such an approach will generate the evidence needed to demonstrate compliance with the requirements of ISO 9001, the part of a process that addresses the requirements is identified in the tables that follow.

ISO 9001:2000 CLAUSE	CLAUSE TITLE	BUSINESS PROCESS	PROCESS ELEMENT
4	Quality management system		
4.1	General requirements	Business management	Business planning
		All processes	Process activities
4.2	General documentation requirements		
4.2.1	System documentation	All processes	Process activities
4.2.2	Quality manual	Business management	Business planning
4.2.3	Control of documents	All processes	Process activities
4.2.4	Control of records	All processes	Process activities
			Review & improvement
5	Management responsibility		
5.1	Management commitment	Business management	Business planning
		All processes	Policies & objectives
5.2	Customer focus	Business management	Business planning
		Marketing	Marketing activities
		Sales	Sales activities
5.3	Quality policy	Business management	Business planning
5.4	Planning		
5.4.1	Quality objectives	All processes	Policies and objectives
5.4.2	Quality management system planning	Business management	Business planning
5.5	Responsibility, authority and communication		

ISO 9001:2000 CLAUSE	CLAUSE TITLE	BUSINESS PROCESS	PROCESS ELEMENT
5.5.1	Responsibility and authority	HR Management	Process activities
5.5.2	Management representative	Business management	Business planning
5.5.3	Internal communication	All processes	Process activities
			Review & improvement
5.6	Management review		
5.6.1	General	All processes	Review & improvement
5.6.2	Review input	All processes	Review & improvement
5.6.3	Review output	All processes	Review & improvement
6	Resource management		
6.1	Provision of resources	All processes	Process activities
6.2	Human resources		
6.2.1	General	HR management	Process activities
6.2.2	Competence, training and awareness	HR management	Process activities
6.3	Infrastructure	Physical resource maintenance	Process activities
6.4	Work environment	Business management	Business policies
			Business planning
		Physical resource management	Physical resource management activities
7	Product realization		
7.1	Planning of product realization	Business management	Business planning
7.2	Customer-related processes		
7.2.1	Determination of requirements related to the product	Marketing	Marketing activities
		Sales	Sales activities
7.2.2	Review of requirements related to the product	Sales	Sales activities
7.2.3	Customer communication	Marketing	Marketing activities
		Sales	Sales activities

ISO 9001:2000 CLAUSE	CLAUSE TITLE	BUSINESS PROCESS	PROCESS ELEMENT
7.3	Design and development		
7.3.1	Design and development planning	Product development	Process activities
7.3.2	Design and development inputs	Product development	Process activities
7.3.3	Design and development outputs	Product development	Process activities
7.3.4	Design and development review	Product development	Process activities
7.3.5	Design and development verification	Product development	Process activities
7.3.6	Design and development validation	Product development	Process activities
7.3.7	Control of design and development changes	Product development	Process activities
7.4	Purchasing		
7.4.1	Purchasing process	Purchasing	Process activities
7.4.2	Purchasing information	Purchasing	Process activities
7.4.3	Verification of purchased product	Purchasing	Process activities
7.5	Production and service provision		
7.5.1	Control of production and service provision	Production	Process activities
7.5.2	Validation of processes for production and service provision	Production	Review & improvement
7.5.3	Identification and traceability	Production	Process activities
7.5.4	Customer property	Production	Process activities
7.5.5	Preservation of product	Distribution	Process activities
7.6	Control of monitoring and measuring devices	All processes	Process activities
			Review & improvement
8	Measurement, analysis and improvement		
8.1	General	All processes	Review and improvement
8.2	Monitoring and measurement		
8.2.1	Customer satisfaction	Business management	Achievement of business objectives

ISO 9001:2000 CLAUSE	CLAUSE TITLE	BUSINESS PROCESS	PROCESS ELEMENT
8.2.1 (Cont:)		Marketing	Achievement of marketing objectives
		Sales	Achievement of sales objectives
8.2.2	Internal audit	All processes	Process effectiveness
8.2.3	Monitoring and measurement of processes	All processes	Process activities
			Process effectiveness
8.2.4	Monitoring and measurement of product	Purchasing	Process activities
			Achievement of objectives
		Production	Process activities
			Achievement of objectives
8.3	Control of nonconforming product	Purchasing	Process activities
		Production	Process activities
8.4	Analysis of data	All processes	Achievement of objectives
			Process effectiveness
8.5	Improvement		
8.5.1	Continual improvement	All processes	Process effectiveness
8.5.2	Corrective action	All processes	Process activities
			Achievement of objectives
8.5.3	Preventive action	All processes	Process activities
			Process effectiveness

Appendix B

Clause alignment with the key questions

The process approach focuses on performance rather than conformity. However, as indicated throughout this book, in order to conform with ISO 9001 organizations need to demonstrate their processes are being effectively managed and this means being able to answer the five key questions. Some of the links between these five key questions were included in the commentary following each question in Chapters 5 & 6. A more comprehensive alignment with the clauses of ISO 9001 is presented in the table below, thus demonstrating that the five key questions do provide an effective means of gathering evidence needed to confirm conformity with all the requirements of ISO 9001.

KEY PROCESS QUESTION	BASE CLAUSE	RELATED CLAUSES	
What are you trying to do?	5.3 Quality policy	5.3a	Ensuring quality policy is appropriate to organization's purpose
		6.4	Determining the work environment
	5.4.1 Quality objectives	4.2.3b	Ensuring documents are up to date
		5.1c	Ensuring quality objective are established
		5.1a	Establishing statutory and regulatory requirements
		5.2	Determining customer needs and expectations
		7.1	Product quality objectives and requirements
		7.2.1	Determination of requirement related to the product
		7.3.2	Design and development inputs
How do you make it happen?	4.1a Identify processes	5.1	Commitment to development of a QMS
		5.4.2	QMS planning and change management
		6.2	Human resources
		6.3	Infrastructure
		7.1	Planning of product realization
		7.2.3	Customer communication
		7.3.1	Design and development planning
		7.4.1	Purchasing process

KEY PROCESS QUESTION	BASE CLAUSE	RELATED CLAUSES	
	4.1a Identify processes (cont:)	7.5	Control of production and service provision
		8.1	Monitoring, measurement, analysis and improvement processes
	4.1b Determine sequence and interaction of processes	6.2	Human resources
		6.3	Infrastructure
		7.1	Planning of product realization
		7.2.3	Customer communication
		7.3.1	Design and development planning
		7.4.1	Purchasing process
		7.5.1	Control of production and service
		8.1	Monitoring, measurement, analysis and improvement processes
How do you make it happen? (cont:)	4.1c Develop criteria & methods	5.5.1	Responsibility and authority
		5.5.2	Management representative
		7.1	Planning of product realization
		7.4.1	Purchasing process
		7.5.1	Control of production and service provision
		7.5.3	Identification and traceability
		7.5.4	Customer property
		7.5.5	Preservation of product
		8.1	General
		8.3	Control of nonconforming product
		8.5.3	Preventive action
	4.1d Provide information	4.2.1	General documentation requirements
		4.2.2	Quality manual
		4.2.3	Control of documents
		4.2.4	Control of records
		5.1	Communicating importance of meeting requirements
		5.3	Communication of quality policy
		5.5.3	Internal communication
		7.1	Planning of product realization
		7.2.3	Customer communication
		7.3.3	Design and development outputs
		7.4.2	Purchasing information

KEY PROCESS QUESTION	BASE CLAUSE	RELATED CLAUSES	
How do you make it happen? (cont:)	4.1d Provide resources	5.1e)	Commitment to ensuring availability of resources
		6.1	Provision of resources
		6.2	Human resources
		6.3	Infrastructure
		6.4	Work environment
		7.1	Planning of product realization
How do you know it's right?	8.2.4 Monitor and measure product	7.3.4	Design and development review
		7.3.5	Design and development verification
		7.3.6	Design and development validation
		7.4.3	Verification of purchased product
		7.5.1	Implementing monitoring and measuring
		7.6	Control of monitoring and measuring devices
		8.1a	Implement processes to monitor and measure conformity of product
		8.2.1	Customer satisfaction
	4.1e Monitor and measure processes	5.5.2	Reporting on performance of the QMS
		5.6	Review of system adequacy
		7.5.2	Validation of processes
		8.1	Implement processes to monitor and measure conformity of the QMS
		8.2.2	Audit QMS for conformity with planned arrangements
		8.2.3	Monitoring and measurement of processes
	8.4 Analyse product and process	8.1	Implement analysis processes
		8.5.2	Corrective action
		8.5.3	Preventive action
		8.3	Control of nonconforming product
	4.1f Implement actions to achieve planned results	5.6	Management review
		7.3.7	Control of design changes
		8.1	Implement measurement processes
		8.2.3	Monitoring and measurement of processes
		8.5.1	Continual improvement
		8.5.2	Corrective action
		8.5.3	Preventive action

KEY PROCESS QUESTION	BASE CLAUSE	RELATED CLAUSES	
How do you know it's the best way of doing it?	4.1e Monitor and measure processes	5.6	Review for continued suitability
		5.6.3	Review resource needs
		7.6	Control of monitoring and measuring devices
		5.3	Review of quality policy for continued suitability
		8.1	Implement monitoring, measurement processes
		8.2.2	Audit QMS for effective implementation and maintenance
		8.2.3	Monitoring and measurement of processes
	4.1e Analyse processes	8.1	Implement analysis processes
		8.4	Analysis of data for system suitability
	4.1f Continually improve processes	8.1	Implement improvement process
		8.5.1	Continual improvement of processes
How do you know it's the right thing to do?	4.1e Monitor and measure processes	5.6	Review of system for continued effectiveness
		5.1	Commitment to continually improving system effectiveness
		7.2.2	Review of requirements related to the product
		8.1	Implement processes to monitor and measure effectiveness of the QMS
	4.1e Analyse processes	5.6.2f	Changes that could affect the QMS
		7.6	Control of monitoring and measuring devices
	4.1f Continually improve processes	5.6	Need to change quality policy and objectives
		5.5.3	Communication of system effectiveness
		8.1	Implement processes to improve effectiveness of the QMS
		8.5.1	Implement improvement process

About the authors

David Hoyle has over 29 years experience in quality management. He held managerial positions with British Aerospace and Ferranti International and as a management consultant; firstly, with Neville-Clarke Ltd and before forming Transition Support Ltd, as an independent, he guided such companies as General Motors, Civil Aviation Authority and Bell Atlantic through their ISO 9000 programmes. He delivered quality management and auditor training courses throughout the world and published five books with Butterworth Heinemann on ISO 9000, some of which have been translated into Spanish, Japanese and Mandarin. Worldwide sales of his first book, now in its third edition, have reached over 25,000 copies. He participates in various committees of the Institute of Quality Assurance and has been engaged in the revision of ISO 9000. He is a Chartered Engineer, Fellow of the Institute of Quality Assurance, an IRCA registered Lead Auditor and Member of the Royal Aeronautical Society.

John Thompson is an experienced management consultant in business improvement and over a 20 year period held management positions in Unilever, RHP Bearings, Mars and Caradon. During the last 12 years, and prior to forming Transition Support Ltd, he was in management consultancy as a Director of Neville-Clarke Ltd and GPR Consultants Ltd. He assisted organizations in Europe, the Middle East and South East Asia in their business improvement activities, including the use of ISO 9000 Baldrige, Singapore Quality Award and EFQM frameworks. He has assisted many organizations develop improvement strategies and apply the process approach to system development and to auditing, including the Anchor Trust, Mars, TRW and MAFF and is an adviser to the MTTA on their step change initiative. Initially trained as a Statistician, he has undertaken post-graduate studies in Business Administration and is currently completing an MA in Human Resource Management.

About Transition Support

Transition Support is committed to assisting organizations achieve improved business performance. Our approach to publications is to create a vision of the future and take readers on a journey along which their perceptions will change and by which they will identify new opportunities - in reality a transition that takes the readers from where they are to where they would like to be. Readers will benefit by saving time, gaining knowledge and tools to aid the endeavour.

You can find out more from our web site http://www.transition-support.com

Other publications from Transition Support

❑   Quality management principles ~ A Self assessment guide

❑   Converting a Quality Management System using the Process Approach

❑   Transition to ISO 9001:2000 ~ Analysis of the differences and implications

❑   ISO/TS 16949 Gap Analysis

❑   Process approach to auditing

Other services from Transition Support

❑   Training

    o   ISO 9000:2000

    o   ISO/TS 16949

    o   Management system auditing

    o   Process management

❑   Management consultancy

Feedback

We would welcome feedback from readers about this book and suggestions for improvement. You can contact us in the following ways:

Tel/Fax: 44 (0)1600 716509 or + 44 (0)1242 525859

E-mail: mail@transition-support.com

S-mail: Our mailing address is on page ii.